GCSE
Questions and Answers

CHEMISTRY

KEY STAGE 4

Bob McDuell & Graham Booth

Chief Examiners

Letts
EDUCATIONAL

SERIES EDITOR: BOB McDUELL

Contents

HOW TO USE THIS BOOK

The aim of the *Questions and Answers* series is to provide you with help to do as well as possible in your exams at GCSE or, in Scotland, at General and Credit levels. This book is based on the idea that an experienced Examiner can give, through examination questions, sample answers and advice, the help students need to secure success and improve their grades.

This *Questions and Answers* series is designed to provide:

- Introductory advice on the different types of questions and how to answer them to maximise your marks.
- Information about the other skills, apart from the recall of knowledge, that will be tested on examination papers. These are sometimes called **Assessment Objectives** and include communication, problem solving, evaluation and interpretation (see pages 4–6). The *Questions and Answers* series is intended to develop these skills by showing you how marks are allocated.
- **Revision Summaries** to remind you of the topics you will need to have revised in order to answer examination questions.
- Many examples of **examination questions**, arranged by topic, with spaces for you to fill in your answers, just as on an examination paper. Only try the questions once you have revised a topic thoroughly. Read the Revision Summary before attempting the questions to double-check you know the topic. It is best not to consult the answers before trying the questions.
- **Sample answers** to all of the questions.
- **Advice from Examiners**. By using the experience of actual Chief Examiners we are able to give advice on how you can improve your answers and avoid the most common mistakes.

THE IMPORTANCE OF USING QUESTIONS FOR REVISION

Past examination questions play an important part in revising for examinations. However, it is important not to start practising questions too early. Nothing can be more disheartening than trying to do a question which you do not understand because you have not mastered the topic. Therefore, it is important to have studied a topic thoroughly before attempting any questions on it.

How can past examination questions provide a way of preparing for the examination? It is unlikely that any question you try will appear in exactly the same form on the papers you are going to take. However, the Examiner is restricted on what can be set because the questions must cover the whole syllabus and test certain Assessment Objectives. The number of totally original questions that can be set on any part of the syllabus is very limited and therefore similar ideas occur over and over again. It certainly will help you if the question you are trying to answer in an examination is familiar and you know you have done similar questions before. This is a great boost for your confidence and confidence is what is required for examination success.

Practising examination questions will also highlight gaps in your knowledge and understanding which you can go back and revise more thoroughly. It will also indicate which sorts of questions you can do well and which, if there is a choice of questions, you should avoid.

Attempting past questions will get you used to the type of language used in questions.

Finally, having access to answers, as you do in this book, will enable you to see clearly what is required by the Examiner, how best to answer each question, and the amount of detail required. Attention to detail is a key aspect of achieving success at GCSE.

EXAMINATION TECHNIQUE

Success in GCSE examinations comes from proper preparation and a positive attitude to the examination. This book is intended to help you overcome 'examination nerves' which often come from a fear of not being properly prepared. Examination technique is extremely important and certainly affects your performance. Remember the basics:

● Read the questions carefully.

● Make sure that you watch the time carefully and complete the paper. It is no good answering one question well if you spend so long doing it that you do not answer another question at all.

● Read the rubric on the front of the examination paper carefully to make sure you know how many questions to attempt.

● Examination papers usually tell you how many marks are available for each answer. Take notice of this information as the number of marks gives a guide to the importance of the question and often to the amount which you ought to write.

● Check before the end of the examination that you have not missed any pages. Remember to turn over the last page, too.

● Remember to leave time to check through your work carefully.

HOW ARE THE EXAMINATIONS DIFFERENT IN 1998?

There are new Chemistry syllabuses throughout England, Wales and Northern Ireland based upon the revised National Curriculum. The syllabuses in Scotland remain unchanged.

The biggest difference is the replacement of three tiers – Basic, Intermediate and Higher – by a two tier system: Foundation and Higher. The table shows the grades available on the two tiers.

FOUNDATION	HIGHER
	A*
	A
	B
C	C
D	D
E	
F	
G	

Under the present system, grades are available outside the accepted range for exceptional performance. An Intermediate tier candidate doing exceptionally well could be given a grade A even though the paper was not targeted above grade B. This will not be possible from 1998. A candidate who fails to achieve a grade D on the Higher paper will be ungraded or one who achieves 100% on the Foundation tier cannot be given a grade above C.

It is most important that you are entered for the correct tier. If you expect to achieve A*, A or B you should of course, enter the Higher tier. If you have any doubt about getting a grade C or D you should enter the Foundation tier to avoid the risk of being ungraded.

The papers will have approximately 20% of marks targeted at each of the available grades. So, a Higher tier paper will have approximately 20% of marks targeted at A*, at A, at B, at C and at D, Foundation tier papers will have 20% of marks targeted at C, at D, at E, at F and at G. The questions targeted at C and D on the two papers will largely be the same. This means that the hardest questions on the Foundation tier are likely to be the easiest questions on the Higher tier. It is intended that these common questions (about 40–45% of each paper) will help to ensure that the performance expected for C and D will be the same on the two tiers.

GCSE Chemistry papers will be set using syllabuses based upon National Curriculum Science Attainment Target 3. However, each Examination Board has added extra material and this varies from Board to Board. The amount of extra material is less than for the syllabuses used in 1996-7. You should check carefully what this extra material is by looking at a copy of your syllabus. Your teacher will have one or you can contact the Examination Board for a copy.

Another difference in 1998 is the use of questions which test your ability to write continuous and extended answers to questions. Approximately 20% of the marks must be awarded to questions requiring longer answers by the candidate. An extended answer is one requiring two sentences to answer it. A continuous answer is one requiring longer answers, perhaps three, four or more sentences.

In this book there are many examples of questions requiring extended and continuous answers so you can see what is required. You are not penalised if your answers are not written in complete sentences and there are no marks added for your correct use of spelling, punctuation and grammar. If you are short of time you should write your answers in short notes rather than try writing extended prose. When you write continuous or extended prose, do not be tempted to fill out your answer.

It is a waste of your time and will not score marks. Try and look for logical links to the points you are making and put the points into a logical order.

Types of examination question

The questions used on GCSE papers are Short Answer and Structured Questions of varying lengths. Most of the questions in this book are of this type. The reason they are used so widely is because they are so versatile. They can be short, with little opportunity for extended writing but giving good syllabus coverage. This makes them very suitable for questions testing lower grades on Foundation tier papers. Alternatively, they can be longer and more complex in their structure, with opportunities for extended writing and the demonstration of higher level of interpretation and evaluation. In this form they are very suitable for questions targeted at A* and A grades on Higher level papers.

In a structured question, the question is divided into parts (a), (b), (c), etc. These parts can be further subdivided into (i), (ii), (iii), (iv), etc. A structure is built into the question and hence into your answer. This is where the term structured question comes from.

For each part of the question there are a number of lines or a space for your answer. This is a guide to you about the detail required in the answer, but it does not have to limit you. If you require more space continue your answer on a separate sheet of paper, but make sure you label the answer clearly, e.g. 3(a)(ii).

For each part of the question there is a number in brackets, e.g. (3), to show you how many marks are allocated to this part of the question by the examiner. If a part is worth three marks, for example, the question requires more than one or two words. As a general rule, if there are three marks allocated, you will need to make three points.

To give you a guide as you work through structured questions, papers are often designed to enable you to score one mark per minute. A question worth a maximum of fifteen marks should therefore take about fifteen minutes to answer.

You do not have to write your answers in full sentences. Concise notes are often the most suitable response.

Like all questions, it is most important to read the stimulus material in the question thoroughly and more than once. This information is often not used fully by students and, as a result, the question is not answered fully. The key to answering many of these questions comes from the appreciation of the full meaning of the 'command word' at the start of the question – 'state', 'describe', 'explain'. The following glossary of command words may help you in the answering of structured questions.

- **State** This means a brief answer is required, with no supporting evidence. Alternatives include **write down**, **give**, **list**, **name**.

- **Define** Just a definition is required.
- **State and explain** A short answer is required (see **state**) but then an explanation is required. A question of this type should be worth more than one mark.
- **Describe** This is often used with reference to a particular experiment. The important points should be given about each stage. Again this type of question is worth more than one mark.
- **Outline** The answer should be brief and the main points picked out.
- **Predict** A brief answer is required, without supporting evidence. You are required to make logical links between various pieces of information.
- **Complete** You are required to add information to a diagram, sentence, flow chart, graph, key, table, etc.
- **Find** This is a general term which may mean calculate, measure, determine, etc.
- **Calculate** A numerical answer is required. You should show your working in order to get an answer. Do not forget the correct units.
- **Suggest** There is not just one correct answer, or you are applying your answer to a situation outside the syllabus.

Grid questions

These are another type of multiple-choice question used on Chemistry papers by the Scottish Examination Board.

In these questions you have to circle the appropriate letter or letters in the answer grid, e.g.

A CH_4	B H_2	C CO_2
D CO	E C_2H_5OH	F C

(a) Identify the hydrocarbon(s).
*[The question does not tell you whether one or more than one substance is required. The only correct answer is **A** and you should circle this letter in the grid. A hydrocarbon is a compound of hydrogen and carbon only. If you circle too many answers you lose marks.]*

(b) Identify the substance(s) which can burn to produce **both** carbon dioxide and water.
*[Again the question does not tell you how many answers to give. The correct answers are **A** and **E** – the only ones where carbon and hydrogen are combined together.]*

ASSESSMENT OBJECTIVES IN CHEMISTRY

Assessment Objectives are the intellectual and practical skills you should be able to show. Opportunities must be made by the Examiner when setting the examination paper for you to demonstrate your mastery of these skills when you answer the question paper.

Traditionally, the Assessment Objective of knowledge and understanding has been regarded as the most important skill to develop. Candidates have been directed to learn large bodies of knowledge to recall in the examination. Whilst not wanting in any way to devalue the learning of facts, it should be remembered that on modern papers knowledge and understanding can only contribute about half of the marks available. The other half of the marks are acquired by mastery of the other Assessment Objectives. These are:

- To communicate scientific observations, ideas and arguments effectively.

- To select and use reference materials and translate data from one form to another.
- To interpret, evaluate and make informed judgements from relevant facts, observations and phenomena.
- To solve qualitative and quantitative problems.

1 Communicate scientific observations, ideas and arguments effectively
(*weighting on papers approximately 5–10%*)

In any examination, communication of information to the Examiner is of primary importance. Questions are built into the paper to test your ability to communicate scientific information. Often these questions require extended answers.

In this type of question it is important to look at your answer objectively after you have written it to try to judge whether your answer is communicating information effectively.

2 Select and use reference materials and translate data from one form to another (*weighting on papers approximately 10–15%*)

In questions testing this Assessment Objective you are frequently asked to pick information from a chart or table and use it in another form, e.g. to draw a graph, a pie chart, bar chart, etc. You may be asked to complete a table using information from a graph.

It is important to transfer the skills you have acquired in Mathematics to your work in Chemistry.

Skill acquired	Approx. grade in GCSE Maths
Read information from graphs or simple diagrams	F
Work out simple percentages	F
Construct and use pie charts	F
Use graphs	E
Plot graphs from data provided. The axes and scales are given to you	E
Be able to draw the best line through points on a graph	C
Select the most appropriate axes and scales for graph plotting	B

It is reasonable, therefore, to conclude that at Higher level you might be required to use a blank piece of graph paper and choose your own scales and axes. Then you would plot the points and draw a line of best fit through the points. If you are doing this, remember:

❶ To draw your graph as large as possible on the graph paper by choosing scales appropriately. Avoid choosing scales where, for example, 3 small squares are equivalent to 5°C. It would be better if 1 small square was equivalent to 1°C or 2°C. With this type of graph drawing, marks are usually awarded for the choice of scales and for labelled axes.

❷ To plot each point with a dot or small cross. Circle the dot or cross to make its position clear.

❸ Your line of best fit, whether it is a straight line or a curve, does not have to go through all the points. Some points may not be in the correct place, even if you plotted them correctly, because of inaccuracies in the experiment or experimental error.

On a Foundation tier paper a similar graph may have to be drawn, but it would be more appropriate for the Examiner to give a grid with axes and scales given. Then you would only have to plot the points and draw the line of best fit.

3 Interpret, evaluate and make informed judgements from relevant facts, observations and phenomena (*weighting on papers approximately 10–15%*)

Questions testing this Assessment Objective are often difficult for candidates. It is much easier to test this on a Higher tier paper than on a Foundation tier paper.

The command word 'suggest' is very frequently used, as the information given, perhaps in a paragraph or a table or a diagram or any combination of these, is open to more than one interpretation.

Look carefully at all of the information given and look for possible alternative interpretations before writing your answer.

4 Solve qualitative and quantitative problems (*weighting on papers approximately 10–15%*)

There is no shortage of opportunities to ask questions testing this Assessment Objective on Chemistry GCSE papers. Again opportunities are greater, especially for solving quantitative problems, on Higher tier papers.

Qualitative problems can include writing equations and the use of qualitative tests, for example, to distinguish sulphuric and hydrochloric acids.

Quantitative problems include the full range of chemical calculations – which, for generations, have baffled students studying Chemistry. Remember, when attempting to carry out a chemical calculation, to:

❶ Use all of the information given to you. If the question gives relative atomic masses, they should be used.

❷ Show all of your working, so credit can be given if you do not get the correct answer but get some way through the question.

❸ Take care when substituting in a mathematical formula to be consistent in your units.

❹ Give correct units to your answers if there are units. Remember ratios, including relative atomic masses, do not have units.

Throughout this book you will see questions where the question is designed to test Assessment Objectives other than knowledge and understanding.

There are three states of matter – **solid**, **liquid** and **gas**. All matter can exist in any of these states depending upon conditions of temperature and pressure. In all three states the material is made up of particles

In a solid the particles are vibrating about fixed positions. If the solid is crystalline the particles are regularly arranged and usually closely packed. In a liquid the particles are still close together but there is no regular arrangement. There is more movement of particles and the movement gets more as temperature rises. In the gas state the particles have broken away from each other and are free to move around.

When a change of state occurs, e.g. solid to liquid, there is an associated energy change. In this case energy is required to break up the solid structure and give the particles additional kinetic energy. The reverse process – liquid to solid – will release energy. **Diffusion** is the movement of particles to spread out and fill all of the available space. Diffusion takes place rapidly with gases because the particles in a gas are moving rapidly. It takes place more slowly in liquids and solids because there is less movement of particles.

Elements are composed of atoms. A piece of iron is made up solely of iron atoms. In a mixture there will be different types of atom and the atoms of the different elements will not be joined. In a compound again there will be atoms of different elements but they will be joined together. A mixture of hydrogen and oxygen can consist of hydrogen and oxygen in different proportions but water, a compound of hydrogen and oxygen, contains always twice as many atoms of hydrogen as oxygen. Groups of atoms in elements or compounds are called **molecules**. An oxygen molecule consists of a pair of oxygen atoms together, O_2, and a water molecule, two hydrogen atoms and one oxygen, H_2O.

Atoms of the different elements are made up of different numbers of protons, neutrons and electrons. An atom always contains an equal number of protons and electrons. If an atom loses one or more electrons it forms a **positive ion** or **cation**. If an atom gains one or more electrons it forms a **negative ion** or **anion**. Atoms of the same element must contain the same number of protons and electrons but can contain different numbers of neutrons. These are called **isotopes**. The protons and neutrons make up the positively charged nucleus and the electrons move around the nucleus.

There are two methods commonly used to join or **bond** atoms together. **Ionic bonding**, e.g. sodium chloride, involves the complete transfer of one or more electrons from a metal atom to a non metal atom. This forms ions which are held together by strong electrostatic forces. **Covalent bonding**, e.g. chlorine or hydrogen chloride, involves the sharing of pairs of electrons.

The properties of a material are related to the structure of the material. If the material is made up of molecules it will have a low melting and boiling point. If it is made up of a **giant structure** of atoms or ions, it will have a high melting point. A giant structure of ions produces a melt which conducts electricity.

Chemical reactions which release energy are called **exothermic** reactions and ones which take in energy are called **endothermic** reactions. These can be represented in energy level diagrams.

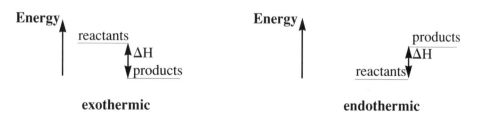

exothermic　　　　　　　　　**endothermic**

When chemical bonds are broken, energy is used, and energy is produced when bonds are formed. If a reaction is exothermic (gives out energy) the energy produced by the bonds formed is greater than the energy required to break the bonds.

If you need to revise this subject more thoroughly, see the relevant topics in the *Letts* GCSE *Chemistry Study Guide*, or *CD-ROM*.

1 The diagrams show the outer electron arrangements in atoms of hydrogen and chlorine.

hydrogen atom

chlorine atom
(not to scale)

(a) Draw diagrams to show the arrangement of the outer electrons in

(i) a hydrogen molecule, H_2

(ii) a chlorine molecule, Cl_2 (2)

(b) What type of bonding is present in both a hydrogen molecule and a chlorine molecule?

.... (1)

(c) Explain why the boiling point of chlorine is greater than the boiling point of fluorine, F_2, but less than the boiling point of bromine, Br_2?

....

....

.... (3)

(d) Dry hydrogen chloride, HCl, is a gas. It dissolves in water producing heat energy and a solution which conducts electricity.
Describe the changes in bonding when dry hydrogen chloride is dissolved in water.

....

....

.... (3)

2 There are two different types of lithium atom $^{6}_{3}$Li and $^{7}_{3}$Li. Lithium has a relative atomic mass of 6.9.

(a) What name is used to describe the different types of lithium atom?

.... (1)

(b) What can be said about the proportions of each type of atom in lithium?

....

....

.... (1)

(c) Complete the table to show the numbers of protons, neutrons and electrons in the $^{7}_{3}$Li^{+} ion.

Particle	Number
protons	
neutrons	
electrons	

(2)

SEB 1995

3 The diagram shows a simple representation of the particles in a gas.

(a) Describe the movement of the particles in a gas.

.... (1)

(b) Why does increasing the temperature of the gas increase the pressure of the gas?

.... (2)

(c) Sulphur dioxide gas and hydrogen sulphide gas react. The symbolic equation is

$$2H_2S\,(g) \;+\; SO_2\,(g) \;\rightarrow\; 3S\,(s) \;+\; 2H_2O\,(l)$$

QUESTIONS

A long tube was clamped horizontally. A pad of cotton wool soaked in hydrogen sulphide solution (giving off hydrogen sulphide gas) and a pad soaked in sulphur dioxide solution (giving off sulphur dioxide gas) were placed at the same time in opposite ends of the tube.

After five minutes a band of whitish solid was formed inside the tube.

(i)   What is the whitish solid formed in the tube?

.... (1)

(ii) The solid formed because of the movement of hydrogen sulphide and sulphur dioxide particles. What is this movement of particles called?

.... (1)

(iii) What does the experiment tell you about the movement of hydrogen sulphide and sulphur dioxide particles?

.... (1)

(iv) Why does it take so long for the band of solid to form?

....

.... (2)

4   The table gives some of the properties of six substances A–F.

Substance	Density (g per cm³)	Melting point (°C)	Boiling point (°C)	Electrical conductivity	Other properties
A	0.97	98	883	conductor	forms a basic oxide
B	3.51	> 3550	4827	non-conductor	forms an acidic oxide
C	2.25	3680	4827	conductor	forms an acidic oxide
D	3.12	−7	59	non-conductor	does not burn
E	0.001	−169	−104	non-conductor	burns to form CO_2 and H_2O only
F	2.17	801	1413	non-conductor when solid; conductor when molten	dissolves in water

(a) Using the information in the table, write down the letter of the substance that

   (i)   is a liquid at room temperature and pressure   ....

   (ii) has the most widely spaced particles   ....

   (iii) is a metal   ....

   (iv) is a solid which floats on water   ....

   (v) has a giant ionic structure   ....

   (vi) has a giant atomic (macromolecular) structure   ....   (6)

   (You can use a letter once, more than once or not at all)

(b) B and C are different forms of the same element in the same state.

   (i)   What name is given to the different forms of the same element in the same state?

   .... (1)

   (ii) What evidence is there in the table that B and C are the same element?

   .... (1)

   (iii) What evidence is there that B and C are non-metallic?

   .... (1)

2 Oil and Carbon Chemistry

The study of the chemistry of carbon compounds, excluding some simple compounds such as carbon dioxide and carbon monoxide, is called **organic chemistry**. There is a very large number of carbon compounds because of the stable bonds formed by carbon atoms with other carbon atoms and with atoms of a range of other elements.

Petroleum (crude oil) is a source of hydrocarbons widely used in the chemical industry. Fractional distillation separates petroleum into different fractions, each containing a number of chemical compounds which boil within a range of temperature.

Most of the compounds making up petroleum are **alkanes**. These are a homologous series of **hydrocarbons** (compounds of carbon and hydrogen only) which all fit a general formula of C_nH_{2n+2}. The simplest members are:

H | H – C – H | H	H H | | H – C – C – H | | H H	H H H | | | H – C – C – C – H | | | H H H	H H H H | | | | H – C – C – C – C – H | | | | H H H H	H H H | | | H – C – C – C – H | | | H H | H – C – H | H
CH_4 methane	C_2H_6 ethane	C_3H_8 propane	C_4H_{10} n-butane	isobutane

There are two **isomers** of butane because alternative arrangements of the atoms are possible. All alkanes are **saturated**, i.e. they contain only carbon–carbon single bonds. Alkanes make good fuels, but are otherwise unreactive.

Cracking is used to break long-chain alkanes into smaller molecules. The products of cracking depend upon conditions. Some of the molecules produced are **unsaturated** and belong to the homologous series of **alkenes**. Alkenes fit a general formula C_nH_{2n} and contain a carbon–carbon double bond. The simplest alkene is ethene, C_2H_4. The presence of a carbon–carbon double bond (or triple bond) can be detected by using bromine dissolved in a suitable solvent (e.g. hexane). The bromine solution turns from red-brown to colourless.

Alkenes are much more reactive than alkanes. Like alkanes they burn, but they also take part in addition reactions, e.g.

ethene + hydrogen → ethane   ethene + water → ethanol

Manufacturing margarine is an important industrial process which uses the addition of hydrogen to unsaturated molecules. Animal and vegetable oils, the raw material, contain carbon–carbon double bonds and are liquid. The corresponding saturated compounds are suitable for use as margarine as they are solid. Hydrogen gas is passed through the oil in the presence of a nickel catalyst at 140 °C. Hydrogenation (reaction with hydrogen takes place).

Ethanol (sometimes called alcohol) can be produced from ethene by an addition reaction. It can also be produced by **fermentation**. Fermentation is the action of enzymes on a solution of sugar or starch.

$$C_6H_{12}O_6 \rightarrow 2C_2H_5OH + 2CO_2$$

glucose   ethanol   carbon dioxide

The solution produced by fermentation is a dilute solution of ethanol in water. The ethanol can be made more concentrated by fractional distillation.

**REVISION
SUMMARY**

Many of the items which used to be made from metals are now made of plastic materials called **polymers**. There are many polymers which exist in nature, e.g. cellulose, starch and proteins. They are called **natural polymers**. Probably more important to us today for manufacturing items are factory-made **synthetic polymers**. Examples are poly(ethene), polystyrene and nylon. There are two types of polymerization – **addition polymerization** and **condensation polymerization**.

In addition polymerization the monomers contain a carbon–carbon double bond. The molecules join together without losing any atoms.

$$nM \rightarrow (M)_n$$

An example of addition polymerization is making poly(ethene).

$$n \left(\begin{array}{c} H \\ \\ H \end{array} C = C \begin{array}{c} H \\ \\ H \end{array} \right) \longrightarrow \left[\begin{array}{cc} H & H \\ | & | \\ C - C \\ | & | \\ H & H \end{array} \right]_n$$

The polymer does not contain the double bond present in the monomer.

When condensation polymerization takes place, the monomer molecules lose small molecules, such as water or hydrogen chloride, when they join together. The monomer molecules must contain two reactive groups. Nylon-6,6 is made from polymerizing hexane-1,6-diamine and hexanedioic acid. The process is summarized as

$$H_2N - \Box - NH_2 \qquad HOOC - \bigcirc - COOH \longrightarrow$$
hexane-1,6-diamine   hexanedioic acid

$$\cdots - \overset{O}{\overset{||}{C}} - NH - \Box - NH - \overset{O}{\overset{||}{C}} - \bigcirc - \overset{O}{\overset{||}{C}} - NH - \Box - NH - \overset{O}{\overset{||}{C}} - \bigcirc - \cdots$$

Polymers can be divided into two classes, depending on how they change on heating. **Thermoplastics** soften on heating and then turn solid again on cooling. They are therefore easily moulded. **Thermosetting** polymers do not melt on heating, but at a higher temperature may burn or decompose.

Starch is a natural polymer made in green plants by photosynthesis. Starch is a carbohydrate (a compound of carbon, hydrogen and oxygen fitting a formula $C_xH_{2y}O_y$), made by linking together glucose molecules. Glucose is the monomer and a water molecule is eliminated each time a link is made. Starch is broken down in the digestive system by hydrolysis. The enzyme in saliva (amylase) breaks down the starch to produce a sugar called maltose (two glucose units joined together). Hydrolysis with acid produces glucose.

Proteins are made by joining together monomer molecules called amino acids. There are about 20 amino acids which join together to form proteins. The links between amino acids are called peptide links.

If you need to revise this subject more thoroughly, see the relevant topics in the *Letts* GCSE *Chemistry Study Guide*, or *CD-ROM*.

QUESTIONS

1   An organic compound, X, contains only the three elements carbon, hydrogen and oxygen. It contains 37.5% carbon and 12.5% hydrogen.
$(A_r(C) = 12, A_r(H) = 1, A_r(O) = 16)$

(a) Use the information to find the empirical formula of X.   (4)

X can be oxidized, under suitable conditions, to form an acid, Y.

(b) Suggest a structural formula for X.   (1)

(c) What homologous series does X belong to?

.... (1)

(d) Suggest an identity for the acid Y.

.... (1)

2   By-products fom the manufacture of petrol include methane, CH_4, ethene, C_2H_4 and ethyne, C_2H_2.

(a) (i) Ethene reacts with steam in the presence of a catalyst by **addition.**
         Explain what the term addition means in this reaction.

....

....

.... (2)

(ii) Why is the reaction of ethene with steam so important commercially?

....

.... (1)

(b) Ethyne reacts with hydrogen chloride to produce the monomer, chloroethene, C_2H_3Cl. This monomer is also called vinyl chloride.

   (i) Deduce a structural formula for this monomer.

(1)

   (ii) Vinyl chloride can undergo **polymerization**.

   1 What is meant by the term polymerization in this reaction?

   ....

   .... (1)

   2 What is the important characteristic of the structure of vinyl chloride which allows it to act as a monomer?

   .... (1)

   3 Give the structure of the polymer formed from vinyl chloride.

(2)

(c) In 1994 it was suggested that the price of petrol should be doubled, to deter its use because of the impact of pollution on the environment.

   Name **two** different pollutants produced by using petrol as a fuel.

   ....

   .... (2)

QUESTIONS

Suggest what could be done to cut down the emission of each of these pollutants, so that petrol could still be used as a fuel.

....

....

....

.... (2)

MEG 1996

3 The flow chart outlines some useful products which can be obtained from crude oil. Crude oil is a mixture of hydrocarbons.

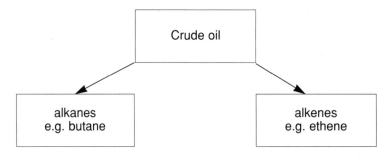

(a) (i) The molecular formula of butane is C_4H_{10}. Draw a structural formula for butane.

(1)

(ii) The molecular formula for ethene is C_2H_4. Draw a structural formula for ethene.

(1)

(b) Ethene and butane react with bromine:

$$C_2H_4 + Br_2 \rightarrow C_2H_4Br_2$$

$$C_4H_{10} + Br_2 \rightarrow C_4H_9Br + HBr$$

(i) State the conditions needed for each reaction.

Reaction with ethene ....

....

Reaction with butane ....

.... (2)

(ii) Name the type of reaction when bromine reacts with:

ethene..

butane.. (2)

(iii) Draw the full structural formula of each organic product, showing all bonds.

Product from reaction with ethene

Product from reaction with butane

(2)

(c) (i) Write a balanced chemical equation for the combustion of butane in oxygen.

.... (2)

(ii) Use your equation to calculate the volume of oxygen needed to burn 1 dm^3 of butane at room conditions. (1 mole of gas occupies 24 dm^3 at room conditions.)

answer... (2)

SEG 1996

4 (a) Describe the manufacture of aqueous ethanol from a carbohydrate starting material. Your answer should include the name of a suitable starting material, the conditions required and an equation.

....

....

....

....

....

....

....

....

....

.... (8)

(b) How can the solution of ethanol be concentrated? Explain what this method of separation depends on.

....

....

.... (3)

(c) People express different opinions on the desirability of alcoholic drinks being easily available. Give ONE social advantage and ONE disadvantage of the easy availability of alcoholic drinks.

Advantage ....

....

Disadvantage ....

.... (2)

(d) Methylated spirit contains ethanol but must never be drunk. Explain why.

....

....

.... (2)

LONDON 1995

There are three parts which make up the Earth – the **crust**, the **mantle** and the **core**. The crust is a thin layer of surface rocks, between 7 km and 40 km thick. Underneath the crust is the mantle and in the centre of the Earth is the core. Our understanding of the structure of the core comes from studies including the passage of sound waves through the Earth. These studies, called seismic studies, show scientists that the inner core of the Earth is solid.

The work of Alfred Wegener showed that the Earth's crust is made up from a number of huge **plates** which are floating on the liquid magma. Originally the plates made up one supercontinent called the Pangaea. These plates are moving very slowly – perhaps only a few centimetres a year. The movement of these plates is called **plate tectonics**.

Where two plates are sliding past each other, they produce stresses and strains which may be released suddenly in an **earthquake**. When two plates are moving apart, a crack will appear in the Earth's crust. Molten rock from the mantle will come to the surface and new rocks will be formed. This often takes place under oceans and is not easily seen. This is called a **constructive plate margin**.

When two plates collide, rocks are squeezed together. This causes the pushing of one plate upwards to create a mountain range. The Himalayas were formed from the collision of the Eurasian and Indian plates. Alternatively, one of the plates is pushed back downwards into the magma. This is called a **destructive plate margin**.

The rocks of the Earth can be classified as igneous, metamorphic and sedimentary.

- **Igneous rocks** are formed when molten magma from inside the Earth is cooled. They are crystalline and the size of the crystals depends upon the rate of cooling. Large crystals are formed when the cooling is slow. There are two types of igneous rocks – **intrusive** rocks (e.g. granite), which are formed inside the Earth, and **extrusive** rocks (e.g. basalt), which are formed on the surface of the Earth.

- **Metamorphic rocks** are formed when high temperatures and pressures act on sedimentary and igneous rocks. Marble is a metamoporhic rock produced from limestone.

- **Sedimentary rocks** are formed when rocks in the Earth are eroded and the sediments are transported and deposited. When these layers of rock fragments are compressed over a long period, sedimentary rocks are formed. Chalk is a sedimentary rock.

Rocks are being continuously recycled in the rock cycle.

Rocks are used for a wide range of purposes – for building materials and as a source of raw material for making useful products. Metals are extracted from metal ores. The method of extraction is related to the reactivity of the metal.

Most metals react with oxygen, water and acids, but at different rates. Metals are often arranged in order of reactivity, called a **reactivity series**.

Such a series is:

K   Na   Ca   Mg   Al   Zn   Fe   Pb   Cu   Ag

decreasing reactivity

A reactivity series can be used to predict the products of a chemical reaction.

e.g. copper(II) sulphate + iron → copper + iron(II) sulphate

A reaction takes place because iron is more reactive than copper (higher in the reactivity series).

Metals high in the reactivity series are extracted from their ores by electrolysis. **Electrolysis** involves the **decomposition** of an **electrolyte** using electricity. Electrolysis takes place when ions are free to move when an electrolyte is molten or dissolved in water. The products of electrolysis are formed at the electrodes.

e.g. lead(II) bromide (molten) → lead   +   bromine
                                    (formed at the negative   (formed at the positive
                                    electrode called the   electrode called the
                                    cathode)   anode)

Metals and hydrogen are usually produced at the cathode and oxygen or one of the halogens at the anode. Ionic equations are often used to represent changes taking place at the electrodes.

Cathode: $Pb^{2+} + 2e^- \rightarrow Pb$ Anode: $2Br^- \rightarrow Br_2 + 2e^-$

Metals in the middle of the reactivity series are usually extracted by reduction of the ore with carbon. Metals low in the reactivity series are often found uncombined in the Earth or are extracted simply by heating.

Questions on the extraction of the metals aluminium and iron are frequently asked on GCSE Chemistry papers.

Extraction of aluminium

Bauxite is the ore of aluminium. It contains hydrated aluminium oxide $Al_2O_3 3H_2O$. The ore is purified to produce alumina-pure aluminium oxide, Al_2O_3. Aluminium is high in the reactivity series and aluminium oxide is difficult to split up. Electrolysis has to be used.

Aluminium is obtained by the electrolysis of alumina dissolved in molten cryolite (sodium aluminium fluoride, Na_3AlF_6). The anode and cathode are made of carbon.

The electrode reactions taking place are:

Cathode: $Al^{3+} + 3e^- \rightarrow Al$
Anode $2O^{2-} \rightarrow O_2 + 4e^-$

The carbon anode burns in the oxygen produced and has to be regularly replaced. Aluminium is tapped off from the cells.

The process takes a great deal of electricity. To produce 1 tonne of aluminium requires 17 000 kW of electricity, enough electricity for the consumption of a good sized town for 1 hour.

REVISION SUMMARY

If you need to revise this subject more thoroughly, see the relevant topics in the *Letts* GCSE *Chemistry Study Guide*, or *CD-ROM*.

Extraction of iron

Iron is extracted in a continuous process in a blast furnace. The blast furnace is loaded with iron ore (haematite, Fe_2O_3), coke and limestone. The furnace is heated with blasts of hot air. The reactions taking place are:

1. $C + O_2 \rightarrow CO_2$
2. $CO_2 + C \rightarrow 2CO$
3. $Fe_2O_3 + 3CO \rightarrow 2Fe + 3CO_2$
4. $CaCO_3 \rightarrow CaO + CO_2$
5. $CaO + SiO_2 \rightarrow CaSiO_3$

In the important step 3 iron(III) oxide is reduced to iron by carbon monoxide. Impurities such as silicon dioxide are removed from the furnace in step 5 where basic and acidic oxides react to form calcium silicate which is called slag.

Molten impure iron (called pig iron) and molten slag are tapped off at the bottom of the furnace.

Most of the pig iron produced is turned into steel. In the steel making process, oxygen gas is blown through molten iron to convert impurities such as carbon, sulphur and phosphorus into acidic oxides which escape as gases or react with added calcium oxide. Scrap iron can be added to the steel making furnace to reduce the amount of pig iron required. Finally, carbon can be added to produce steel with the required specification.

Steel is an **alloy** of iron, i.e. a mixture of iron with small quantities of carbon and possibly other metals. The addition of small quantities of other metals or carbon alters the properties of iron. High carbon steel is strong but brittle. Low carbon steel is soft and is easily shaped. Stainless steel which contains chromium and nickel is hard and resistant to corrosion.

1   The Earth's surface is the top of a solid crust which is made up of plates. These plates move slowly. The crust under the continents is about 35 km thick and has an average density of about 2.7 g/cm³. The crust under the ocean floor is much thinner and has an average density of about 3.3 g/cm³. The material underneath the crust has an average density of about 4.5 g/cm³.
The average density of the Earth is 5.5 g/cm³.

(a) What evidence is there to suggest that there is a dense metal core at the centre of the Earth?

....

.... (1)

(b) Continental plates often collide with ocean floor plates. Describe what is likely to happen when a continental plate meets an ocean plate moving in the opposite direction. Explain your answer. A diagram may help you with your answer.   (3)

(c) Explain how earthquakes can occur where two plates meet together.

....

.... (2)

(d) What evidence suggests that there may be molten material underneath the Earth's crust?

.... (1)

(e) The map shows the 'supercontinent' called the Pangaea.

How does the theory of plate tectonics explain the existence of similar fossils and rocks in South America and Africa?

....

.... (2)

2 This question is about rocks in the Earth and the way they are recycled. The following diagram may help you with your answers.

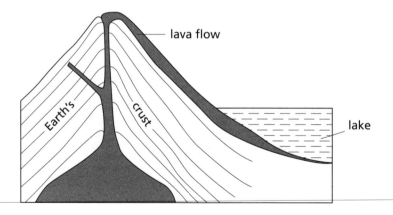

(a) Explain why igneous rocks may contain bubbles and crystals of different sizes.

....

....

.... (3)

(b) Why do different compounds separate as different layers in the lake?

....

....

.... (3)

(c) What is the driving force of the rock cycle?

.... (1)

(d) Outline three processes which cause rocks to be weathered.

1 ....

2 ....

3 .... (3)

(e) Describe the processes which take place to turn an igneous rock into a metamorphic rock.

....

....

.... (3)

3 The diagram below represents some of the natural processes at work in forming rocks.

(a) (i) Why are basalt and granite referred to as igneous rocks?

....

.... (1)

    (ii) Explain why crystals in basalt are smaller than crystals in granite.

....

....

.... (1)

(b) Water may collect in small cracks in the surface of rocks.
At times it will freeze, thawing again when the temperature rises.
Explain how this freezing and thawing process causes weathering of rocks.

....

.... (2)

(c) (i) Give an example of a sedimentary rock.

.... (1)

    (ii) Using the diagram to help you, explain the process by which sedimentary rocks
form.

....

....

....

....

.... (3)

MEG 1995

---

4   (a) Lead is extracted from lead(II) sulphide.
Lead(II) sulphide is roasted in air to produce lead(II) oxide and sulphur dioxide gas.
The lead(II) oxide is then heated in a blast furnace with coke (carbon).

    (i) Write an equation for the reaction of lead(II) sulphide and oxygen.

.... (2)

(ii) Explain why it would be damaging to the environment to allow the sulphur dioxide to escape into the atmosphere.

....

....

....

.... (2)

(iii) Suggest why lead extraction plants are sometimes sited near to chemical works where sulphuric acid is made.

....

....

.... (1)

(b) The equation for the reaction which occurs when lead(II) oxide is heated in a blast furnace with coke is given below.

$$2PbO + C \rightarrow 2Pb + CO_2$$

(i) What type of chemical process does the lead(II) oxide undergo in this reaction?

.... (1)

(ii) Assuming that a tonne of coke contains 90% of usable carbon, calculate how much coke is needed to extract the lead from 10 tonnes of lead(II) oxide.

....

....

....

.... (5)

(c) The lead contains about 1.2 kg of silver per tonne of lead. The silver is removed by adding about 2% of zinc to molten lead in a furnace at about 800 K.

Here is some data to consider.
    The melting point of lead is 601 K; the melting point of zinc is 693 K.
    Zinc is less dense than lead.
    Zinc and lead do not mix when molten.
    Silver is much more soluble in molten zinc than in molten lead
    Silver-zinc mixtures have much higher melting points than either pure zinc
    or pure lead.
    Silver-zinc mixtures are less dense than molten lead.

(i) Write **true** or **false** after each of these statements.

The silver will dissolve mostly in the zinc...

A silver-lead mixture will form on top of the zinc. ....

Lead will float on top of a silver-zinc liquid mixture ....

A silver-zinc mixture will form on top of molten lead. .... (2)

(ii) Why do you think so much trouble is taken to remove such a small amount of silver from each tonne of lead?

....

.... (1)

(d) Here is some data about some salts

lead(II) chloride	insoluble in cold water (20° C) soluble in hot water
lead(II) nitrate	soluble in hot and cold water
sodium chloride	soluble in hot and cold water

(i) Starting from lead(II) nitrate and sodium chloride, describe how you would obtain some well-shaped crystals of lead(II) chloride.
Include essential practical details and give an equation for any reaction taking place.

....

....

....

....

....

....

.... (4)

(ii) Why does the reaction of lead(II) oxide and cold hydrochloric acid stop very quickly?

....

.... (1)

MEG 1996

5   **The extraction of metals from their treated ores are redox (oxidation-reduction) reactions. Different methods are used for iron and aluminium.**

Explain the two sentences above by writing an account of the extraction of iron and aluminium. Your answer should be about the redox processes taking place. You should give relevant redox equations There will be no marks for detailed descriptions of the processes.

....

....

....

....

....

....

....

....

....

....

....

.... (8)

Air is a mixture of gases. The most common gas in the air is nitrogen and this is very unreactive. The active gas in the air is oxygen. The composition of the air varies but a typical composition of air is: nitrogen 78.1 %; oxygen 21.0 %; argon 0.09 %; carbon dioxide 0.03 %; traces of neon, krypton and xenon.

The gases in the air can be separated by fractional distillation of liquid air. Liquid air is allowed to warm up and nitrogen boils off before oxygen because it has a lower boiling point. Oxygen has a wide range of uses including for breathing equipment and in steel making. Much of the nitrogen produced is turned into fertilizers. Noble gases, such as argon, are very unreactive and are used to fill light bulbs.

Processes such as combustion, rusting and respiration use up oxygen in the air. Green plants replace oxygen by the process of photosynthesis. These processes are summarised in the carbon cycle.

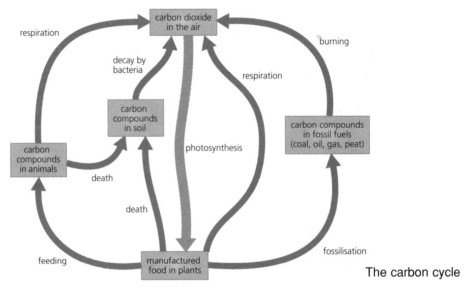

The carbon cycle

Air pollution

NORMAL COMPOSITION OF DRY AIR (by volume)	
nitrogen	78.1%
oxygen	21.0%
argon	0.9%
carbon dioxide	0.03%
Traces of neon krypton xenon	

The normal composition of air is given on the left. Other gases get into the air and can alter the volume composition of air. Probably the most serious pollutant of air has been sulphur dioxide, which is produced when fuels containing sulphur are burned. Coal, in particular, contains appreciable amounts of sulphur and so produces sulphur dioxide on combustion. When sulphur dioxide gets into the air it is oxidized and, in the presence of water, produces sulphuric acid. It is probably the most important cause of **acid rain**. Acid rain makes lakes and rivers too acidic, killing off fish and other water-life, causes the death of trees and vegetation, erosion of stonework, corrosion of metals, etc. As the amount of sulphur dioxide in the atmosphere is being reduced, as a result of restrictions on the burning of coal, desulphurization processes in coal-fired power stations and the use of other means of generating electricity, another pollutant is becoming very serious. This is nitrogen oxide, which is produced, along with carbon monoxide, in car exhausts. Many of the effects of nitrogen oxide are similar to those of sulphur dioxide.

Burning fuels containing carbon efficiently to produce carbon dioxide is not without its problems. As we burn more of these fuels the levels of carbon dioxide in the atmosphere are increasing. This produces the **greenhouse effect**, where energy from the Sun reaches the Earth and cannot be re-radiated. As a result, the temperature of the Earth is rising and this will have effects on climate, etc.

The use of chlorofluorocarbons (CFCs) as refrigerants and in aerosol sprays is now being controlled, as these chemicals, when they are released into the atmosphere, destroy the **ozone layer** in the upper atmosphere. It is the ozone layer that shields the Earth from the most powerful ultraviolet rays from the Sun.

1 This question is about the process of photosynthesis which goes on in green plants.

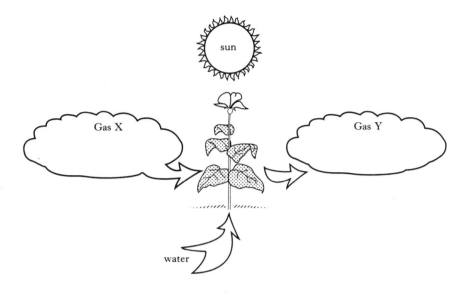

(a) Write down the names of the gases X and Y in the diagram.

Gas X   ....

Gas Y   .... (1)

(b) Explain the job of photosynthesis in keeping the composition of the atmosphere constant.

....

.... (2)

SEB 1995

2 A scientist analysed the fumes emitted from a factory chimney.
The fumes contained these substances.

carbon dioxide

carbon monoxide

carbon particles

sulphur dioxide

water

(a) Which substance in the list causes most global warming?

.... (1)

(b) Methane is a gas which also causes global warming.
Name **one** source of methane pollution.

.... (1)

QUESTIONS

(c) Five years after the factory was built, the stonework of a building nearby started to crumble.

Suggest how the factory might have caused this.

....

....

.... (2)

(d) The graph shows the average levels of sulphur dioxide in the atmosphere.

New laws about air pollution were passed in 1956 and 1968.

What evidence is there that the 1968 law had more effect than the 1956 law?

....

....

.... (2)

MEG 1995

3   The table gives some information about the physical properties of five carbon compounds.

Name	Formula	Melting point (°C)	Boiling point (°C)	Density as a liquid (g per cm³)
Cyclohexene	C_6H_{10}	−103	83	0.81
Dichlorodifluoromethane	CCl_2F_2	−158	−30	1.40
Ethane	C_2H_6	−183	−89	0.57
Methane	CH_4	−182	−164	0.47
Propane	C_3H_8	−190	−42	0.58

Use the data to help you answer the following questions.

(a) Which of the compounds has the lowest melting point?

.... (1)

(b) Dichlorodifluoromethane is a chlorofluorocarbon (CFC). CFCs are liquids under pressure. They vaporize rapidly when the pressure is reduced to atmospheric pressure. CFCs can be used as propellants in aerosol sprays.

   (i) Draw a diagram to show the arrangement of outer electrons in a molecule of dichlorodifluoromethane.   (2)

   (ii) What type of bonding exists in a molecule of dichlorodifluoromethane?

   .... (1)

   (iii) Why is there concern about the quantities of CFCs being released into the atmosphere?

   ....

   ....

   .... (3)

   (iv) Which one of the compounds in the table would you choose as an alternative to dichlorodifluoromethane in aerosol sprays? Give your reasons.

   Compound...

   Reasons .... (2)

Understanding quantitative aspects of Chemistry is important on papers at higher levels. The following important terms need to be understood.

Relative atomic mass, A_r

This is the number of times the mass of one atom of an element is heavier than the mass of one-twelfth of a carbon-12 atom (or approximately the mass of a hydrogen atom).

The mole

A mole is the amount of substance which contains 6×10^{23} particles (Avogadro's number). 1 mole of copper, for example, contains the same number of particles as 1 mole of sulphur atoms and twice as many particles as 0.5 moles of magnesium. The mass of 1 mole of an element or a compound can be found using relative atomic masses.

E.g. mass of 1 mole of   (a) copper, Cu;   (b) oxygen atoms, O;   (c) oxygen molecules, O_2;
                          (d) calcium carbonate, $CaCO_3$;   (e) calcium hydroxide, $Ca(OH)_2$.

(a) $A_r(Cu) = 64$.   Mass of 1 mole of copper atoms = 64 g

(b) $A_r(O) = 16$.   Mass of 1 mole of oxygen atoms = 16 g

(c) Mass of 1 mole of oxygen *molecules* = 32 g

(d) $A_r(Ca) = 40$, $A_r(C) = 12$, $A_r(O) = 16$.
Mass of 1 mole of calcium carbonate = $40 + 12 + (3 \times 16) = 100$ g

(e) $A_r(Ca) = 40$, $A_r(O) = 16$, $A_r(H) = 1$.
Mass of 1 mole of calcium hydroxide = $40 + 2(16 + 1) = 74$ g

You can calculate the number of moles of a substance by dividing the mass of the substance by the mass of 1 mole.

Molar volume

One mole of molecules of any gas occupies a volume of $24\,dm^3$ at room temperature and atmospheric pressure.

Molar solution

A solution containing 1 mole of solute dissolved to make $1\,dm^3$ of solution is called a molar solution (M solution). A 2M solution contains 2 moles of solute in each cubic decimetre of solution.

Empirical formula

This is the simplest formula of a compound in which the atoms are in the correct ratio. CH_2 is the empirical formula for C_2H_4, C_3H_6, C_4H_8, etc. To get the molecular formula it is necessary to know the mass of 1 mole (or relative molecular mass).

The formula of a compound can be obtained from the reacting masses of the reactants.
E.g. 6.0 g of carbon combines with 1.0 g of hydrogen.
Converting into numbers of moles:

6.0/12 moles of carbon atoms combines with 1.0/1 moles of hydrogen atoms.
0.5 moles of carbon atoms combines with 1 mole of hydrogen atoms.
Empirical formula is CH_2.
If the mass of 1 mole is 28 g, the molecular formula is C_2H_4.

The formula of a compound can be obtained in a similar way from percentages. If you are told that a compound of only iron, sulphur and oxygen contains 28% iron and 24% sulphur, you could work out the percentage of oxygen by difference. It is the same as the previous calculation, but using 28 g Fe, 24 g S, and 48 g O.

The percentage of an element present in a compound can be found from the mass of the

**REVISION
SUMMARY**

element present and the mass of 1 mole of the compound. For example, the percentage of nitrogen in ammonium nitrate, NH_4NO_3, can be found if we know that $A_r(N) = 14$, $A_r(H) = 1$, $A_r(O) = 16$.

Mass of 1 mole of ammonium nitrate $= 14 + 4 + 14 + (3 \times 16) = 80\,g$
Mass of nitrogen present $= 2 \times 14\,g$
Percentage of nitrogen $= 100 \times 28/80 = 35\%$

Balanced symbolic equations can be used for calculating the quantities of reacting substances and products.

E.g. $CaCO_3 + 2HCl \rightarrow CaCl_2 + H_2O + CO_2$

The equation tells us that 1 mole of calcium carbonate (100 g) combines with 2 moles of hydrochloric acid (71 g or $2\,dm^3$ of M solution) to form 1 mole of calcium chloride (111 g) and 1 mole of water (18 g) and 1 mole of carbon dioxide (44 g). Note the sum of the masses of the reactants always equals the sum of the masses of the products.

Calculating the concentration of a solution
E.g. what is the molar concentration of a solution of hydrochloric acid containing 7.3 g of hydrogen chloride in $100\,cm^3$ of solution. $(A_r(H) = 1$, $A_r(Cl) = 35.5)$
Mass of 1 mole of hydrogen chloride, HCl, $= 1 + 35.5 = 36.5$ (Unit 6)
7.3 g of hydrogen chloride in $100\,cm^3$ of solution has the same molar concentration as 73 g of hydrogen chloride in $1000\,cm^3$ of solution. The solution contains 73/36.5 moles of hydrogen chloride. The solution is 2 M (or $2\,moles/dm^3$).
A solution of known concentration is called a **standard solution**. Using a standard solution of hydrochloric acid, the concentration of a sodium hydroxide solution can be found by titration. The symbolic equation

$NaOH(aq) + HCl(aq) \rightarrow NaCl(aq) + H_2O(l)$

tells us that 1 mole of sodium hydroxide reacts with 1 mole of sodium hydroxide. The hydrochloric acid is put into a burette. Exactly $25\,cm^3$ of sodium hydroxide solution is added to a conical flask using a pipette, and a couple of drops of screened methyl orange (or other suitable indicator) is added to the contents of the flask. The solution is now green. Hydrochloric acid is added from the burette until the solution just goes violet. This is called the **end point**. The solution is now neutral. Adding extra acid now would change the indicator pink. The volume of acid added can now be recorded and the process repeated.

> If you need to revise this subject more thoroughly, see the relevant topics in the *Letts* GCSE *Chemistry Study Guide*, or *CD-ROM*.

1 (a) Vinegar is a dilute aqueous solution of ethanoic acid. The concentration of ethanoic acid in vinegar can be determined by titration with sodium hydroxide solution. The equation for the reaction is

$$CH_3COOH + NaOH \rightarrow CH_3COONa + H_2O$$

In one experiment $10.0\,cm^3$ of vinegar required $22.0\,cm^3$ of sodium hydroxide solution of concentration 0.50 mole/dm^3 (mole per litre) for neutralization.

(i) Calculate the number of moles of sodium hydroxide present in $22.0\,cm^3$ of solution.
(2)

(ii) Calculate the concentration of ethanoic acid in vinegar in mole/dm^3 (mole per litre).
(4)

(iii) From your answer to part (ii), calculate the concentration of ethanoic acid in g/dm^3 (g per litre). (Relative atomic masses; H = 1, C = 12, O = 16)
(2)

(b) (i) $0.3\,g$ of magnesium metal was placed in excess ethanoic acid. Calculate the volume of hydrogen gas, measured at room temperature and pressure, which was given off in this reaction. The equation for the reaction is

$$Mg + 2CH_3COOH \rightarrow (CH_3COO)_2Mg + H_2$$

(Relative atomic mass of Mg = 24; 1 mole of gas occupies $24\,000\,cm^3$ at room temperature and pressure)
(4)

(ii) If the concentration of the ethanoic acid used in this experiment was 2.0 mole/dm^3 (mole per litre) calculate the volume of ethanoic acid actually required to completely react with the magnesium.
(4)

(c) Ethanoic acid reacts with ethanol to give an ester.

  (i) Give the name of the ester formed.

  .... (1)

  (ii) Draw the structure of this ester. All bonds must be shown. (2)

(d) (i) Some esters are reacted with alkalis to make soap. What is the natural source of these esters?

  .... (1)

  (ii) Give TWO other uses of esters.

  ....

  .... (2)

  NICCEA 1993

2 This question concerns the electrolysis of molten calcium bromide, $CaBr_2$, using carbon electrodes.

  (a) Draw a labelled diagram of the apparatus used for the electrolysis of molten calcium bromide. Include a switch and a bulb in your circuit. (3)

(b) A current of 5 A is passed for 193 seconds.

   (i) How many coulombs of electricity have passed?

   .... (2)

   (ii) How many Faradays of electricity have passed? (1 Faraday = 96 500 coulombs)

   .... (1)

   (iii) Calcium is produced at the negative electrode by the discharge of Ca^{2+} ions.
        How many moles of calcium atoms were produced?

   .... (2)

   (iv) Bromine is produced at the positive electrode by the discharge of Br^- ions.
        How many moles of bromine atoms were produced at the positive electrode?

   .... (2)

(c) At the end of the experiment the heat was removed and the calcium bromide turned
    solid. The bulb continued to glow. Explain.

   ....

   .... (1)

(d) When the apparatus was washed up at the end of the experiment, bubbles of colourless
    gas were produced. What was the colourless gas and how was it formed?

   ....

   .... (3)

3 Washing soda is hydrated sodium carbonate, $Na_2CO_3.xH_2O$. An experiment was carried out
to find the value of x.
   28.6 g of fresh hydrated sodium carbonate crystals were dissolved in distilled water and
the solution made up to a volume of $1000\,cm^3$. $25\,cm^3$ of this solution was transferred to a
conical flask and a few drops of methyl orange indicator added.
   The solution in the conical flask was titrated with 0.25 M hydrochloric acid
($0.25\,mole/dm^3$) and $20.0\,cm^3$ of acid were required to reach the end point.

(a) Name the most suitable piece of apparatus for measuring out exactly $25\,cm^3$ of sodium
    carbonate solution and transferring it to the conical flask.

   .... (1)

(b) How would you know that the end point of the titration had been reached?

.... (1)

(c) Write a balanced symbolic equation for the reaction of sodium carbonate with dilute hydrochloric acid.

.... (2)

(d) How many moles of hydrochloric acid react with 25 cm³ of sodium carbonate solution?
(2)

(e) How many moles of hydrochloric acid would react with 1000 cm³ of sodium carbonate solution? (2)

(f) Using the equation, how many moles of anhydrous sodium carbonate are present in 1000 cm³ of sodium carbonate solution? (2)

(g) What mass of anhydrous sodium carbonate is present in 1000 cm³ of sodium carbonate solution? (A_r(Na) = 23, A_r(C) = 12, A_r(O) = 16) (2)

(h) Complete the following:

.... g of anhydrous sodium carbonate combines with .... g of water to produce 28.6 g of sodium carbonate crystals. (1)

(i) How many grams of water would combine with 1 mole of sodium carbonate?

.... (1)

(j) What is the value of x? (A_r(H) = 1, A_r(O) = 16)

.... (1)

4 Toners for colouring black-and-white photographs are made by mixing two solutions. The solutions should be made up using warm water.

Solution 1
Sodium sulphide solution concentration 100 g/l

Solution 2
Sodium hydroxide solution concentration 80 g/l

QUESTIONS

(a) Why is **warm** water used to make up the solutions?

.... (1)

(b) Calculate the concentration of sodium hydroxide in mol/l. (2)
Show your working clearly.

(c) Different colours are obtained by mixing the two solutions.

Colour	Volume of sodium suphide solution/cm³	Volume of sodium hydroxide solution/cm³
cold brown	10	40
brown	20	30
warm brown	30	20

What mass of sodium sulphide will be required to make $100\,cm^3$ of toner for a cold brown colour? **Show your working clearly.** (2)

SEB 1995

5 Limestone is impure calcium carbonate. The purity can he found by adding a measured amount of limestone to a measured, excess of dilute hydrochloric acid. The following reaction takes place.

$$CaCO_3(s) + 2HCl(aq) \rightarrow CaCl_2(aq) + H_2O(l) + CO_2(g)$$

(a) (i) State TWO methods by which you could tell that pure calcium carbonate had completely reacted with dilute hydrochloric acid.

1 ....

....

2 ....

.... (2)

(ii) One of these methods is not reliable with impure samples of calcium carbonate such as limestone. State which ones and give a reason for its unreliability.

....

.... (1)

(b) After the limestone has reacted, sodium hydroxide can then be added to neutralise the remaining excess acid. The following reaction takes place.

$NaOH(aq) + HCl\ (aq) \rightarrow NaCl\ (aq) + H_2O\ (l)$

Write the ionic equation for this reaction.

.... (2)

(c) In a determination of the percentage purity of limestone, the following results were obtained.

Mass of hydrochloric acid in solution	=	20.00 g
Mass of limestone	=	25.00 g
Mass of hydrochloric acid left unreacted	=	2.48g

(i) What mass of hydrochloric acid reacted with the limestone?

.... (1)

(ii) Using the equation
$CaCO_3\ (s) + 2HCl\ (aq) \rightarrow CaCl_2\ (aq) + H_2O\ (l) + CO_2\ (g)$, calculate the mass of calcium carbonate with which this mass of hydrochloric acid would react.

....

....

....

....

.... (4)

(iii) Calculate the percentage purity of the limestone (the percentage of pure calcium carbonate in the limestone).

....

.... (1)

London 1995

6 The Periodic Table

The Periodic Table is an arrangement of chemical elements in order of increasing atomic number. Elements with similar properties are in the same vertical column (or group). The horizontal rows are called **periods**.

The Periodic Table was first devised by the Russian chemist Mendeleef in 1869. You will have a copy of this table in your examination to help you. Use this table to check the spelling of the element name, the symbol, the mass number, the atomic number and elements with similar properties. For example, if you wish to know about the chemistry of silicon, you will notice it is in the same group as carbon and this should help you write the formula of its oxide as SiO_2, similar to CO_2.

The table consists of eight groups of elements in the **main block**. These are Groups I to VII and 0.

Group I elements are called the alkali metals and Group VII elements are called the halogens. You need to know the chemistry of the these two groups. Group 0 elements are called the noble gases. Between the two parts of the main block are the elements called **transition metals**. These include iron, nickel and copper.

Metals are on the left hand side of the table and non-metals on the right. There is often a bold stepped line to divide metals from non metals. Elements which are gases at room temperature ant atmospheric pressure, are in the top right hand corner of the table.

Elements with similar chemical properties, i.e. in the same group, have similar outer electron arrangements, e.g. lithium 2,1 and sodium 2,8,1. Apart from the noble gases, the number of electrons in the outer energy level of any element in the main group is the same as the group number of the element.

The table gives the electron arrangement of the first twenty elements in the Periodic Table and the formulae of oxides and chlorides of these elements.

If you need to revise this subject more thoroughly, see the relevant topics in the *Letts* GCSE *Chemistry Study Guide*, or CD-ROM.

element	electron arrangement	formula of oxide	formula of chloride
hydrogen	1	H_2O	HCl
helium	2	------	---------
lithium	2,1	Li_2O	LiH
beryllium	2,2	BeO	BeH_2
boron	2,3	B_2O_3	B_2H_6
carbon	2,4	CO_2	CH_4
nitrogen	2,5	range	NH_3
oxygen	2,6	------	H_2O
fluorine	2,7	F_2O	HF
neon	2,8	-----	----
sodium	2,8,1	Na_2O	NaH
magnesium	2,8,2	MgO	MgH_2
aluminium	2,8,3	Al_2O_3	AlH_3
silicon	2,8,4	SiO_2	SiH_4
phosphorus	2,8,5	P_2O_5	PH_3
sulphur	2,8,6	SO_3	H_2S
chlorine	2,8,7	Cl_2O_7	HCl
argon	2,8,8	------	----
potassium	2,8,8,1	K_2O	KH
calcium	2,8,8,2	CaO	CaH_2

1 The Periodic Table skeleton below contains only four elements, labelled W, X, Y and Z. These are not the chemical symbols of these elements.

															W		V
																Y	
X																	

(a) Which letter represents

   (i)   a halogen?   ....

   (ii) a noble gas?   ....

   (iii) an alkali metal?   ....   (3)

(b) Which element, W, X, Y or Z, has the smallest atoms? Explain your answer.

   Element ....

   Explanation ....

   .... (3)

(c) Write down the formula for the compound formed between

   (i) X and Y   ....

   (ii) X and W   ....   (2)

(d) An element Z combines with magnesium to form a white solid. In an experiment 0.72 g of magnesium reacts with Z to form 1.00 g of the white solid.

   $(A_r(Mg) = 24,\ A_r(Z) = 14)$

   (i) Calculate the formula of the white solid formed.   (3)

(ii) Where in the Periodic Table is the most likely place for the element Z?

Period .... Group................................

Give reasons for your answer.

....

....

.... (4)

2 This diagram shows part of the Periodic Table.
The letters do **not** represent the symbols for the elements.

(a) Identify the alkali metal.

A	B	C	D	E	F

(1)

(b) Identify the element which exists as diatomic molecules.

A	B	C	D	E	F

(1)

(c) Identify the **two** elements which are in the same group.

A	B	C	D	E	F

(1)

SEB 1995

3   The table below gives some of the properties of elements in group II of the Periodic Table

Element	Symbol	Reaction with water	Formula of chloride
Beryllium	Be		$BeCl_2$
Magnesium	Mg	Reacts slowly with cold water, vigorously with steam	$MgCl_2$
Calcium	Ca	Reacts steadily with cold water	$CaCl_2$
Strontium	Sr	Reacts vigorously with cold water	$SrCl_2$
Barium	Ba	Reacts very vigorously with cold water	

(a) Arrange the **four** elements in *italics* in order of reactivity, putting the most reactive first.

   .... (1)

(b) Suggest what would happen when beryllium is added to cold water.

   ....

   .... (1)

(c) Suggest how barium should be safely stored.

   ....

   .... (1)

(d) When barium is heated in chlorine gas they react to form a solid.

   (i) Give the name and formula of the solid formed.

       Name ....

       Formula ....

   (ii) Describe the bonding in the compound.

       ....

       ....

       .... (5)

**REVISION
SUMMARY**

Some chemical reactions are finished in a tiny fraction of a second and some can take millions of years. A reaction which takes place in a very short period of time is called a **fast** reaction. One which takes place over a long period of time is called a **slow** reaction.

The burning of a mixture of hydrogen and oxygen with a squeaky pop is a very fast reaction. The rusting of a steel fence is much slower and the reactions turning vegetable matter into crude oil much slower still. The rate of a chemical reaction can be changed by changing the conditions of the reaction. The souring of milk can be slowed by cooling the milk in a refrigerator.

Factors which speed up a chemical reaction include:

❶ Increasing temperature. As an approximation, in many chemical reactions, a $10°C$ temperature rise, doubles the rate of reaction.

❷ Increasing the concentration of one or more of the reactants. In the reaction of sodium thiosulphate and dilute hydrochloric acid, doubling the concentration of sodium thiosulphate doubles the rate of the reaction. You must be careful as this relationship, of doubling the rate of a reactant, doubling the rate of the reaction, is not true in all cases.

❸ Using a catalyst. A catalyst alters the rate of a chemical reaction without being used up. Usually a catalyst speeds up a reaction. Some catalysts, called negative catalysts or inhibitors, slow down reactions. A common example of a catalyst is manganese(IV) oxide in the decomposition of hydrogen peroxide into water and oxygen.

❹ Using one of the reactants in a more finely powdered form. For example, powdered calcium carbonate reacts much faster with dilute hydrochloric acid than a lump of calcium carbonate of the same mass.

❺ Using light. A mixture of hydrogen and chlorine explodes in sunlight but does not in the dark. Light can provide the initial energy needed to start a reaction. This is called the **activation energy**.

❻ Increasing pressure. This can increase the speed of a reaction involving gases.

Explaining the rate of reaction in a simple particle theory.

You should be able to explain changes in the rate of a chemical reaction in terms of numbers of successful collisions of reacting particles. Increasing the temperature of a reaction mixture speeds up the particles and results in more collisions between particles. It will also result in more collisions where the particles have sufficient energy to react and so the reaction is speeded up.

Increasing the concentration will again result in more particle collisions and therefore the reaction is faster.

A catalyst provides an alternative route for the reaction which needs a lower activation energy. More collisions have this lower energy and so the reaction is faster.

When one of the reactants is powdered, a large surface area is provided. There are therefore more collisions and, as a result, more successful collisions.

Light works in a similar way to heating: providing additional energy and increasing the pressure is the same as increasing the concentration.

If you need to
revise this
subject more
thoroughly,
see the relevant
topics in the
*Letts GCSE
Chemistry
Study Guide*, or
CD-ROM.

Enzymes

Enzymes are **biological** catalysts which control important processes such as fermentation. An enzyme is a protein. Enzymes work only with certain reactions and under certain conditions. For example, catalase will catalyse the decomposition of hydrogen peroxide but at high temperatures the structure of the enzyme is permanently changed (denatured) and it will no longer work.

1   John investigated the reaction of calcium carbonate with hydrochloric acid. The same mass of calcium carbonate and the same volume of acid were used in each experiment.

(a) Identify the experiment in which gas was produced most quickly.

A	B	C	D	E	F

(1)

(b) Identify the **two** arrangements which would have been compared to show the effect of particle size on the rate of the reaction.

A	B	C	D	E	F

(1)

SEB 1995

2   The equation for the reaction between calcium carbonate and hydrochloric acid is

$$CaCO_3(s) + 2HCl(aq) \rightarrow CaCl_2(aq) + H_2O(l) + CO_2(g)$$

	Mass of flask and contents	
Time (min)	Large lumps (g)	Small lumps (g)
0	112.4	111.6
0.5	111.6	109.2
1	111.1	108.3
2	110.2	107.4
3	109.6	107.2
4	109.1	107.2
5	108.7	107.2
6	108.5	107.2

Two different 10.0 g samples of calcium carbonate were reacted at 25 °C with excess hydrochloric acid for a period of 6 minutes. One of the samples was in the form of large lumps and the other consisted of small lumps. The results in the table show how the mass of the flask and contents changed for each sample.

(a) Draw a diagram of apparatus which would be suitable for carrying out this experiment.

(2)

(b) (i) Explain why the mass of each flask and contents decreases.

.... (1)

(ii) Draw **two** graphs on the same set of axes to show how the **total loss of mass** changes with time for each sample. Label the lines 'large lumps' and 'small lumps'. (*You need a piece of 2 mm graph paper here*) (5)

(iii) On the same grid, sketch the graph you would expect to obtain if the experiment was repeated with 10 g of powdered calcium carbonate. Label this graph 'powder'.

(2)

(c) Calculate the volume of hydrochloric acid, of concentration M (1 mole/dm^3), which would react with 10.0 g of calcium carbonate.
(A_r(Ca) = 40, A_r(C) = 12, A_r(O) = 16) (3)

(d) Explain, in terms of particles, why repeating this experiment using the different conditions given would speed up the reaction.

(i) Hydrochloric acid of concentration 2 M instead of M.

....

.... (2)

(ii) Carrying out the experiment at 35 °C rather than 25 °C

....

.... (1)

Industrial processes 8

There are some very important industrial processes involving chemical reactions. In Chapter 2 processes of fractional distillation, cracking and polymerization were considered. In Chapter 3 the extraction of aluminium and iron. In this Chapter two more processes are considered, the manufacture of ammonia by the Haber process and the manufacture of sulphuric acid by the Contact process.

In any question involving an industrial process you are not required to know the technical details of the process. You are required to;
● know the raw materials required and all the products formed:
● understand the chemical principles involved in the process;
● be able to evaluate social, economic, health and safety, a and environmental factors associated with the process.

Contact process for making sulphuric acid

The Contact process is a three-stage process for producing sulphuric acid, probably the most important industrial chemical, from sulphur or sulphur-containing minerals.

In stage 1, the sulphur or sulphur-containing mineral is burnt in air to form sulphur dioxide.

$$S + O_2 \rightarrow SO_2$$

In stage 2, sulphur dioxide and oxygen react together to produce sulphur trioxide.

$$2SO_2 + O_2 \rightleftharpoons 2SO_3$$

This is a reversible reaction, which means that 100% conversion of the reactants into products is impossible. In such a situation an **equilibrium** is set up, where the rate of the forward reaction and the rate of the reverse reaction are the same and the concentrations of the reactants and products remain unchanged. The economic success of the process will depend upon getting the equilibrium to 'move as far as possible to the right', i.e. to get conditions which produce an equilibrium with a high concentration of sulphur trioxide. The optimum conditions are a temperature of about 450 °C and a catalyst of vanadium(V) oxide.

In stage 3, the sulphur trioxide is dissolved in concentrated sulphuric acid to produce oleum (fuming sulphuric acid) which is then diluted with the required amount of water to make concentrated sulphuric acid.

$$SO_3 + H_2SO_4 \rightarrow H_2S_2O_7$$
$$H_2S_2O_7 + H_2O \rightarrow 2H_2SO_4$$

This is preferable to dissolving the sulphur trioxide directly into water.

Haber process for making ammonia

In the Haber process, nitrogen and hydrogen are combined together to form ammonia. Again the reaction is reversible and conditions must be established to get the equilibrium established as far to the right as possible.

$$N_2 + 3H_2 \rightleftharpoons 2NH_3 \qquad \text{Forward reaction exothermic}$$

Nitrogen and hydrogen are mixed together in the proportions of 1 part of nitrogen and 3 parts of hydrogen. The mixture is compressed to a high pressure and passed over a catalyst of finely divided iron at a temperature of about 450 °C.

The best conditions are *high pressure* (there are more molecules on the left-hand side of the equation than on the right and increasing pressure moves the equilibrium to the right) and *low temperature*. (As the forward reaction is exothermic, lowering the reaction temperature moves the equilibrium to the right. However, lowering the temperature slows down the rate of reaction: using a catalyst helps to speed up the reaction but does not affect the position of the equilibrium). Even under these favourable conditions only about 10% of the nitrogen and hydrogen are converted into ammonia. The unreacted gases are recycled.

The ammonia gas is cooled and liquified to remove it from the other gases. Most of the ammonia is used to make nitric acid or nitrogeneous fertilizers.

If you need to revise this subject more thoroughly, see the relevant topics in the *Letts* GCSE *Chemistry Study Guide*, or CD-ROM.

1 The flow diagram refers to processes used in manufacturing important ammonium compounds.

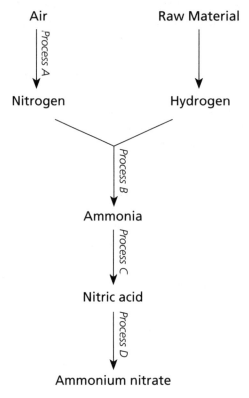

(a) Give the name of

    (i) process A ....

    (ii) process B ....

    (iii) process D .... (3)

(b) What is the major use of ammonium nitrate?

.... (1)

(c) What are the conditions for process B?

....

....

.... (3)

(d) Process C involves a three-stage process for converting ammonia into nitric acid.

Stage 1: Ammonia is mixed with air and the mixture is passed over a heated platinum gauze catalyst. Nitrogen monoxide and steam are produced.

$$4NH_3(g) + 5O_2(g) \rightarrow 4NO(g) + 6H_2O(g)$$

Stage 2: The mixture of gases is cooled and nitrogen dioxide is formed.

$$2NO(g) + O_2(g) \rightarrow 2NO_2(g)$$

Stage 3: The nitrogen dioxide is dissolved in water.

$$4NO_2(g) + 2H_2O(l) + O_2(g) \rightarrow 4HNO_3(l)$$

(i) The platinum gauze has to be heated to start the reaction, but then heating is not necessary. What does this tell you about stage 1?

.... (1)

(ii) What mass of nitric acid could be produced from 17 tonnes of ammonia? ($A_r(H) = 1$, $A_r(N) = 16$, $A_r(O) = 16$)

....

.... (2)

2 (a) Aluminium is extracted from bauxite, a mineral containing alumina, Al_2O_3, and impurities such as iron(III) oxide and silica.

bauxite (4 tonnes)	→ purification →	alumina (2 tonnes)	→ electrolysis →	aluminium (1 tonne)

The electrolysis takes place at about 1000 °C and requires a current of around 100 000 A. In Canada and parts of Scotland, aluminium manufacture takes place near to sources of hydro-electric power. A typical cell is shown below.

(i) Suggest **two** reasons why the extraction of aluminium is an expensive process.

Reason 1 ....

Reason 2 .... (2)

(ii) Describe **three** environmental problems which could be caused by an increase in the world demand for aluminium.

Problem 1 ....

....

Problem 2 ....

....

Problem 3 ....

.... (3)

(b) Oxide ions are discharged at the graphite anodes.

$$2O^{2-} \rightarrow O_2 + 4e^-$$

(i) Write an equation for the discharge of aluminium ions at the cathode.

.... (2)

(ii) If 32 g of oxygen is formed in a particular time, how much aluminium will be formed in the same time? (Relative atomic masses: O = 16, Al = 27)

....

....

....

.... (3)

MEG 1995

Water is a compound of hydrogen and oxygen. The atoms are held together in the water molecule by covalent bonds.

$$O^{\delta-}$$
$$^{\delta+}H \qquad H^{\delta+}$$

Water exists in three states ice, liquid water and water vapour. The changes of state occur at $0°C$ and $100°C$ The boiling point of water is higher than expected because of extra forces holding the molecules together. These are called **hydrogen bonds**.

Water is an extremely good solvent. It dissolves a wide range of different solutes. Usually the solubility of gases in water decreases with increasing temperature. The solubility of solid solutes usually increases with increasing temperature. A graph showing the change in solubility with temperature is called a **solubility curve**. The **solubility** of a solute is the maximum mass of the solute which will dissolve in 100g of water at a particular temperature.

Water supplies

Because water is a very good solvent, it is difficult to get and keep pure. Even as rainwater falls to Earth it dissolves carbon dioxide in the atmosphere and is no longer pure water. When rainwater falls on calcium carbonate rocks, some of the rock reacts with the rainwater.

$$CaCO_3(s) + H_2O(l) + CO_2(g) \rightleftharpoons Ca(HCO_3)_2(aq)$$

This water now contains **temporary hardness**, which can be removed by boiling. If rainwater falls on rocks containing calcium sulphate or magnesium sulphate, they dissolve slightly and the resulting water contains **permanent hardness**, which cannot be destroyed by boiling. Hard water does not lather well with soap but forms a scum. It lathers well with soapless detergents. Permanent hardness can be removed by treatment with chemicals such as washing soda (hydrated sodium carbonate) or the use of ion-exchange resins.

Because it is very difficult to get pure water, no attempt is made to deliver pure water to our homes through a water main. Suitable clean supplies of water are filtered to remove any solid impurities and treated with chlorine to kill any harmful bacteria.

Water pollution is caused by chemicals entering streams and rivers. Many of these chemicals come from farmland, where fertilizers, pesticides, etc. wash off the fields and build up in the water. Nitrogen compounds from sewage and animal waste or from excess fertilizers are a particular problem. Oxidation of ammonia to nitrates uses up the dissolved oxygen in the water. Fish need the oxygen for respiration. Nitrogen and phosphorus compounds in water also encourage the growth of water plants, which prevent light from entering the water. Even nitrates, which were once thought not to be a serious problem have now been shown to be harmful, particularly in drinking water for babies, when in high concentrations. Industry also causes problems, especially if very harmful heavy metals such as lead or cadmium are allowed to escape into rivers.

Sea water is a source of chemicals. Apart from salt which is obtained by evaporation in warmer countries, the sea provides most of the world's supply of magnesium and bromine. Bromine is obtained by acidifying sea water and then bubbling chlorine through it to liberate bromine,which is then obtained by fractional distillation.

$$2NaBr + Cl_2 \rightarrow 2NaCl + Br_2$$

Testing for ions

Analysis means the breaking up into smaller units and is the opposite of **synthesis**. In Chemistry we may carry out **qualitative analysis** to find out what is present.

Carbonate $CO_3{}^{2-}$.
When dilute hydrochloric acid is added to a carbonate, carbon dioxide gas is produced. The carbon dioxide turns limewater milky. No heating is required.

REVISION SUMMARY

Chloride Cl⁻ .

When a solution of a chloride is acidifed with dilute nitric acid and silver nitrate solution is added, a white precipitate of silver chloride is formed immediately This precipitate turns purple in sunlight and dissolves completely in concentrated ammonia solution

Sulphate SO_4^{2-}.

When dilute hydrochloric acid and barium chloride solution are added to a solution of a sulphate, a white precipitate of barium sulphate is formed immediately.

Nitrate NO_3^-.

If sodium hydroxide solution is added to a solution of a nitrate and then aluminium powder is added, a reaction takes place on gentle warming. Hydrogen gas is produced from the reaction of the aluminium and sodium hydroxide. However, if a nitrate is present, ammonia gas is also produced which turns damp red litmus paper blue.

If you need to revise this subject more thoroughly, see the relevant topics in the *Letts* GCSE *Chemistry Study Guide*, or *CD-ROM*.

Ammonium NH_4^+, Aluminium Al^{3+}, Copper(II) Cu^{2+}, Iron(II) Fe^{2+}, Iron(III) Fe^{3+}

These cations can be identified with tests using sodium hydroxide solution. If an ammonium ion is heated with sodium hydroxide solution, ammonia gas is produced.

If sodium hydroxide is added dropwise to solutions of aluminium, copper(II), iron (II) and iron(III) the following results are obtained.

Aluminium.   White precipitate of aluminium hydroxide formed which dissolves in excess sodium hydroxide

Copper(II).   A pale blue precipitate of copper(II) hydroxide is formed.

Iron(II).   A dirty green precipitate of iron(II) hydroxide is formed.

Iron(III) .   A red-brown precipitate of iron(III) hydroxide is formed.

1   Describe how you would distinguish between the following pairs of unlabelled bottles.
    You should state clearly, in any test you suggest, what happens to each of the liquids.
    Credit will be given for relevant equations.

(a) Calcium hydrogencarbonate solution and distilled water.

    ....

    ....

    .... (4)

(b) Sodium carbonate solution and sodium hydroxide solution.

    ....

    ....

    .... (4)

(c) Dilute hydrochloric acid and dilute sulphuric acid.

    ....

    ....

    .... (4)

(d) Hexane and hexene.

    ....

    ....

    .... (4)

2 The table gives some information about four substances which can be used as fertilizers.

Name of compound	Formula	Solubility in water
Ammonium nitrate	NH_4NO_3	very soluble
Ammonium phosphate		soluble
Potassium nitrate	KNO_3	soluble
Urea	$CO(NH_2)_2$	not very soluble but reacts slowly to produce ammonia and carbon dioxide

(a) Complete the table by adding the chemical formula of ammonium phosphate.

(ammonium $= NH_4^+$; phosphate $= PO_4^{3-}$) (1)

(b) A balanced fertilizer can be made by mixing together ammonium phosphate and potassium nitrate. Name three elements which must be present to provide plants with a balanced fertilizer.

.... (1)

(c) Show, by calculation, that urea contains a greater percentage of nitrogen than ammonium nitrate. ($A_r(C) = 12$, $A_r(H) = 1$, $A_r(N) = 14$, $A_r(O) = 16$) (3)

(d) Why might a farmer prefer to use ammonium nitrate?

.... (1)

(e) (i) Write a word equation for the reaction between water and urea.

.... (1)

(ii) Write a balanced symbolic equation for the reaction between water and urea.

.... (3)

(f) Describe possible problems caused by using a soluble fertilizer close to a river.

....

....

....

.... (4)

3 The solubility curve for potassium dichromate, is shown on the grid.

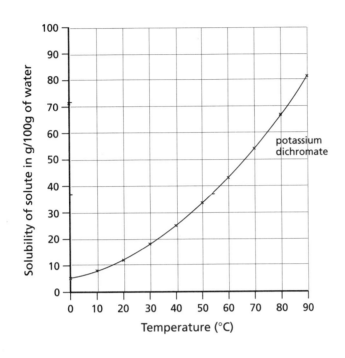

A student wanted to purify some potassium dichromate. She added some potassium dichromate to 100 g of water and heated gently while stirring. The compound just dissolved at 90 °C. The solution was then allowed to cool to 50 °C.

(a) What mass of potassium dichromate was added (ignore impurities)?

.... (1)

(b) What mass of potassium dichromate would still be dissolved when the solution had cooled to 50 °C?

.... (1)

(c) What mass of crystals would be produced after the solution had stopped crystallizing at 50 °C?

.... (1)

(d) How could the student obtain a sample of dry crystals of potassium dichromate from this experiment?

....

.... (2)

4   The label on a bottle of mineral water had the following information.

Ions present		Concentration in g/litre
calcium	Ca^{2+}	0.10
magnesium	Mg^{2+}	0.02
sodium	Na^+	0.01
potassium	K^+	0.01
sulphate	SO_4^{2-}	0.14
hydrogencarbonate HCO_3^-		0.26

(a) (i)   Name a compound which causes temporary hardness in this mineral water.

.... (1)

(ii) Give one method that could be used to remove *permanent* hardness in water.
Explain how this method works.

Method ....

....

Explanation ....

.... (3)

(b) Name the white solid deposit found in kettles which have been used to boil *temporarily*
hard water.

.... (1)

(c) Sodium stearate $C_{17}H_{35}COO^-Na^+$, is a soap. Explain how the scum is formed when this
soap is used in hard water.

....

....

....

.... (3)

SEG 1995

Answers

1 STRUCTURE AND BONDING

Question	Answer	Mark
1 (a)	(i) hydrogen molecule (ii) chlorine molecule	2

(b)	Covalent	1
(c)	Fluorine, chlorine and bromine molecules are similar	1
	Difference in mass: bromine heaviest, fluorine lightest	1
	Heavier molecules need more energy to move them and let them escape from the liquid	1
(d)	Hydrogen chloride (dry) contains a covalent bond	1
	On dissolving in water the hydrogen chloride ionizes *or* forms ions	1
	Ions are H^+ and Cl^- *or better* show the electron arrangement in the ions	1

Examiner's tip You will frequently have to draw simple diagrams to represent atoms. In these diagrams it is usual only to show the nucleus and the outer electrons. If you attempt to show inner electrons incorrectly you may lose marks. This question tests your understanding of covalent and ionic bonding. The change in the bonding of hydrogen chloride takes place when water is present.

2 (a)	Isotopes	1
(b)	Because the relative atomic mass of lithium is 6.9 (closer to 7 than 6), most of the atoms present must be lithium-7.	1

Examiner's tip This question is testing your understanding of the idea of isotopes. You are not expected to calculate the percentage of each isotope in the sample. You would be expected to do this at A level.

(c)

Particle	Number
protons	3
neutrons	4
electrons	2

2

Examiner's tip Two marks are awarded in (c) if all three numbers are correct. One mark is awarded if two are correct. Be careful here. You are asked to work out the numbers of protons, neutrons and electrons in a lithium **ion**. Many candidates will work out the numbers of particles in a lithium atom.

3 (a)	Motion is rapid and random	1
(b)	Particles possess more kinetic energy *or* move faster	1
	More collisions of particles with walls	1

Question	Answer	Mark

> **Examiner's tip** Students frequently consider pressure as collisions between particles and not with the walls of the container.

(c)   (i)   Sulphur   1

     (ii)   Diffusion   1

     (iii)   Hydrogen sulphide particles move about twice as fast as sulphur dioxide particles   1

> **Examiner's tip** The ring of sulphur is closer to one end of the tube than the other. The ring would have formed in the middle if both moved with the same speed. Small (light) particles move faster than large (heavy) particles.

     (iv)   The movement of particles is random and not in one direction only   1
         Particles of air slow the movement of particles down the tube   1

4   (a)   (i)   **D**   1

> **Examiner's tip** Melting point below 20 °C, boiling point above 20 °C.

     (ii)   **E**   1

> **Examiner's tip** Lowest density or is a gas.

     (iii)   **A**   1

> **Examiner's tip** Burns to form a basic oxide.

     (iv)   **A**   1

> **Examiner's tip** Density less than $1.0 \, \text{g/cm}^3$ (density of water).

     (v)   **F**   1

> **Examiner's tip** Conductor when molten and dissolves in water.

     (vi)   **B or C**   1

> **Examiner's tip** **B** is prefered as it is a non-conductor – no chance of ions.

(b)   (i)   Allotropes (or polymorphs)   1

> **Examiner's tip** This question is a data handling question. You do not need a great deal of knowledge. You have to use the information given. Allotropes are often confused with isotopes or isomers

     (ii)   Both have the same boiling point.   1

Question	Answer	Mark

Examiner's tip Both form acidic oxides but they could still be different non-metallic elements.

(iii) Form acidic oxides   **1**

---

2 OIL AND CARBON CHEMISTRY

Question	Answer	Mark

1 (a)   *You might need to refer to Unit 5.*
Percentage of oxygen = 50%   **1**
37.5 g of C combines with 12.5 g of H and 50 g of O
37.5/12 moles of C combines with 12.5/1 moles of H and 50/16 moles of O **1**
3.125 moles C, 12.5 moles H, 3.125 moles O   **1**
Empirical formula is CH_4O **1**

(b)

$$H-\overset{\overset{\displaystyle H}{|}}{\underset{\underset{\displaystyle H}{|}}{C}}-O-H \qquad methanol$$

1

(c)   Alcohols (or alkanols)   **1**

(d)   Methanoic acid HCOOH   **1**

Examiner's tip The oxidation of an alcohol produces an acid. An homologous series is a family of similar compounds with the same general formula. The general formula of alcohols is $C_nH_{2n+1}OH$

---

2 (a)   (i) An addition reaction is the reaction of two molecules to form a single **1**
product. By breaking of double bond between carbons.   **1**

$$\overset{\displaystyle H}{\diagdown}\underset{\displaystyle H}{\diagup}C=C\overset{\displaystyle H}{\diagup}\underset{\displaystyle H}{\diagdown} \quad + \quad HOH \rightarrow \quad H-\overset{\overset{\displaystyle H}{|}}{\underset{\underset{\displaystyle H}{|}}{C}}-\overset{\overset{\displaystyle H}{|}}{\underset{\underset{\displaystyle H}{|}}{C}}-O-H$$

ethanol

(ii) Ethene is produced in large amounts from the cracking of high boiling point oil
fractions. The ethanol produced has a wide range of uses.   **1**

(b)   (i) $\overset{\displaystyle H}{\diagdown}\underset{\displaystyle H}{\diagup}C=C\overset{\displaystyle H}{\diagup}\underset{\displaystyle Cl}{\diagdown}$

1

(ii)   1 Polymerization is the joining of small molecules, called monomers,
together to form long polymer chains.   **1**

2 The presence of a carbon–carbon double bond   **1**

Question	Answer	Mark

3

$$\left[\begin{array}{cc} H & H \\ | & | \\ -C-C- \\ | & | \\ H & Cl \end{array}\right]_n$$

2

One mark is given for the two new bonds linking the monomer to other molecules. One mark is given for the double carbon–carbon bond changing to a single bond.

(c) Carbon monoxide, Nitrogen oxides, Lead, Unburnt hydrocarbons (any two)**2**

The use of excess oxygen (air) will ensure carbon dioxide is produced rather than carbon monoxide.

The use of a catalytic converter converts carbon monoxide and oxides of nitrogen into carbon dioxide and nitrogen

The use of unleaded petrol (one mark for each, max two marks) **2**

Examiner's tip The polymerization of vinyl chloride to form poly(vinyl chloride) is an example of addition polymerization. Part (c) in this question is linked with Chapter 4.

3 (a) (i)

$$H-\overset{\overset{\displaystyle H}{|}}{C}-\overset{\overset{\displaystyle H}{|}}{C}-\overset{\overset{\displaystyle H}{|}}{C}-\overset{\overset{\displaystyle H}{|}}{C}-H$$

1

Examiner's tip There are two possible structures you could draw for butane. These are called isomers. Check back in Chapter 1 that you understand the terms isotope and allotrope which are frequently confused with isomers. The other isomer is

(structure of 2-methylpropane)

(ii)

$$\overset{H}{\underset{H}{>}}C=C\overset{H}{\underset{H}{<}}$$

1

(b) (i) Reaction with ethene. Bubble ethene through a solution of bromine at room temperature. **1**

Reaction with butane. Mix butane and bromine gases in sunlight. **1**

(ii) Addition **1**

Substitution **1**

(iii)

$$Br-\overset{\overset{\displaystyle H}{|}}{C}-\overset{\overset{\displaystyle H}{|}}{C}-Br$$

1

Question	Answer	Mark

$$H-\underset{\underset{H}{\overset{\overset{H}{|}}{|}}{C}-\underset{\underset{H}{\overset{\overset{H}{|}}{|}}{C}-\underset{\underset{H}{\overset{\overset{H}{|}}{|}}{C}-\underset{\underset{H}{\overset{\overset{H}{|}}{|}}{C}-Br$$

| | 1 |

> **Examiner's tip** The names of the two products are 1,2-dibromoethane and bromobutane. They are not required in your answer.

(c) (i) $2C_4H_{10}(g) + 13O_2(g) \rightarrow 8CO_2(g) + 10H_2O(l)$ **2**

> **Examiner's tip** This is a very difficult equation to write. For one mark you must get the correct formulae for the two reactants and the two products. The second mark is for balancing the equation correctly.

(ii) From the equation 2 mole (48 dm³) of butane needs (13 x 24) dm³ of oxygen   **1**

1 dm³ of butane needs 6.5 dm³ of oxygen   **1**

> **Examiner's tip** You will be given two marks for just writing down the answer. One mark will be deducted if you give no units.

---

4 (a)   An aqueous solution of sugar or glucose or starch or sucrose   **1**

In the presence of an enzyme   **1**

Correct named enzyme–zymase   **1**

In the absence of air or oxygen   **1**

Other product is carbon dioxide   **1**

Temperature about 30-40° C   **1**

Fermentation stops when about 13% ethanol present   **1**

$C_6H_{12}O_6(aq) \rightarrow 2C_2H_5OH(aq) + 2CO_2(g)$ **2**

Reaction slightly exothermic   **1**

> **Examiner's tip** There are ten marking points here. You will be given any eight you score. When answering this type of question, read what is required very carefully to make sure you answer it fully.

(b)   Fractional distillation   **1**

Boiling point of ethanol lower than water   **1**

Ethanol boils off before water   **1**

> **Examiner's tip** It is not possible to produce pure ethanol by fractional distillation. You are not expected to know how to produce pure ethanol.

Question	Answer	Mark
(c)	It is not necessary to keep alcohol illegally	1
	Alcohol is available to children/available for alcohol abuse	1
(d)	Methylated spirits is alcohol/contains methanol	1
	Other poisonous substances added to deter drinkers.	1

3 MATERIALS FROM ROCKS

Question	Answer	Mark
1 (a)	Average density is much greater than average density of any rocks of the crust, so there must be high density material in the Earth (core)	1
(b)		3

continental plate   oceanic plate

oceanic plate pushed below continental plate (1) – returns to magma (1)

Examiner's tip There is one mark for the diagram and two for the labels. This is an example of where an annotated diagram is better than a lot of words.

Question	Answer	Mark
(c)	Two plates rub together	1
	Stresses build up which when released produce earthquakes	1
(d)	Hot springs *or* volcanoes	1
(e)	South America and Africa were joined – hence similar rocks	1
	They have moved apart over a long period	1

Question	Answer	Mark
2 (a)	Bubbles caused by gases dissolved in magma	1
	Size of crystals dependent on rate of cooling	1
	Fast cooling – small crystals; slow cooling – large crystals	1

Examiner's tip It is important to relate the size of crystals to the rate of cooling. When liquid magma cools and crystallises slowly, perhaps inside the Earth, large crystals form. When the magma cools and crystallises quickly, perhaps on the surface of the Earth, small crystals are formed.

Question	Answer	Mark
(b)	Particles of different sizes (large particles deposited first)	1
	Different concentrations of dissolved materials	1
	Different solubilities of dissolved materials	1
(c)	Nuclear decay (radioactivity) processes in the Earth	1
(d)	Freezing of water followed by thawing	3
	Wind	(Any 3
	Running water	points)

Question	Answer	Mark

Chemical action due to carbon dioxide or sulphur dioxide
Rubbing of one rock on another

(e)   Erosion of rock. Transport of sediments. Deposition of sediments.
Compaction of sediments to form sedimentary rock. Effect of high
temperature. Effect of high pressure   **3**

Examiner's tip There are six points. Each counts for half a mark. The mark scored is
rounded up if it contains a half mark. Be careful – answers such as temperature
and pressure may not be acceptable without some qualification, e.g. high
temperature or high pressure.

3 (a)   (i)   They are both formed by crystallization of the liquid magma/molten rock. **1**

(ii)   Crystals of basalt are formed near the surface where the rate of cooling
is faster. Granite is formed inside the Earth where cooling is slower.   **1**

(b)   Water enters cracks in the rocks.   **1**

When water freezes, and ice is formed, expansion occurs.
This forces the rock apart. The process repeats over and over again.   **1**

(c)   (i)   Limestone or sandstone or chalk or puddingstone.   **1**

(ii)   Erosion of rocks (igneous, metamorphic or sedimentary) produces small
fragments. These are transported in rivers. When the flow of water slows
in the sea,or a lake, the sediments are deposited and then compacted to
form sedimentary rocks   **3**

Examiner's tip This is a piece of continuous writing. The diagram shows the river and
the sea which should give you some guide.

4 (a)   (i)   Lead(II) sulphide + oxygen → lead(II) oxide + sulphur dioxide

$2\,PbS\,(s) + 3O_2(g) \rightarrow 2\,PbO(s) + 2SO_2(g)$

2

Examiner's tip For grade C or above, on either Foundation or Higher tier, you would
be expected to write a balanced symbol equation. Unless you are very confident, it
is worth writing a word equation first, to help you. Then you have to write the
correct formulae for lead(II) sulphide , oxygen, lead(II) oxide and sulphur dioxide.
Remember, oxygen exists in molecules as pairs of atoms so you have to write O_2.
Finally you have to balance the equation. Notice in the unbalanced equation that
you have three oxygen atoms on the right hand side. This should suggest doubling
the numbers of lead(II) oxide and sulphur dioxide on the right hand side and using
three molecules of oxygen. There are two marks for a correctly balanced equation
and one mark if you make a slight slip, e.g. 6O instead of $3O_2$. The question does
not ask you to include state symbols so there is no mark for them, Include them if
you can as they give a positive impression to the examiner.

(ii)   Sulphur dioxide escaping into the atmosphere can form sulphurous and
sulphuric acids.   **1**
These acids can attack metals and rocks. Also they can make lakes
and rivers more acidic   **1**

Question		Answer	Mark
	(iii)	Sulphur dioxide is a raw material in the manufacture of sulphuric acid.	1
(b)	(i)	Reduction	1
	(ii)	You will need to get relative atomic masses from a Periodic Table	
		$Pb = 208$ and $O = 16$.	
		From the equation,	
		448 tonnes of lead(II) oxide needs 12 tonnes of pure carbon.	1
		So, 10 tonnes of lead(II) oxide needs $12 \times {}^{10}/_{448}$ tonnes of pure carbon.	1
		$= 0.27$ tonnes	1
		However, carbon used is only 90% pure, so amount required is	
		$0.27 \times {}^{10}/_{9}$ tonnes	1
		$= 0.30$ tonnes.	1

> **Examiner's tip** This calculation is very involved and is worth a total of 5 marks. It is important to write down all the steps, to ensure you get full credit and also so marks can be given for correct working even if you get a wrong answer.

Question		Answer	Mark
(c)	(i)	True, false, false, true	2
		All correct two marks, two or three correct one mark	
	(ii)	Silver is a more expensive metal than tin or lead.	1

> **Examiner's tip** It is unlikely that you are familiar with this way of extracting silver. You are not intended to recall knowledge but to use the information in the question.

Question		Answer	Mark
(d)	(i)	Make hot solutions of lead(II) nitrate and sodium chloride.	1
		Mix the hot solutions and allow them to cool slowly	1
		Crystals of lead(II) chloride form on cooling	1
		Filter off the crystals, wash and dry	1
		Lead(II) nitrate + sodium chloride → lead(II) chloride + sodium chloride	
		$Pb(NO_3)_2(aq) + 2NaCl(aq) \rightarrow PbCl_2(s) + 2NaNO_3(aq)$	1
		Count the equation and any three other points	
	(ii)	When pieces of lead(II) oxide react with cold hydrochloric acid, a layer of insoluble lead(II) chloride is formed which prevents the lead(II) oxide and hydrochloric acid coming into contact.	1

> **Examiner's tip** This is an example of a preparation on an insoluble salt by precipitation. It is, however, a difficult example because of the solubility of lead(II) chloride in cold and hot water.

5	**Sample answer**
	The reduction of iron(III) oxide by heating with carbon.
	Carbon monoxide is the active reducing agent. It is produced in the furnace from carbon dioxide

Question	Answer	Mark

$CO_2(g) + C(s) \rightarrow 2CO(g)$

$Fe_2O_3(s) + 3CO(g) \rightarrow 2Fe(l) + 3CO_2(g)$

Iron(III) oxide loses oxygen – hence reduction.

Reduction of aluminium ions by electrolysis of aluminium oxide dissolved in molten cryolite.

At the cathode

$Al^{3+} + 3e^- \rightarrow Al$

Aluminium ions gain electrons and so are reduced.

Aluminium oxide is more difficult to split up than iron oxide. Electrolysis provides more energy than reduction with carbon. **8**

Examiner's tip It is very easy to write at length about the extraction of iron and aluminium. This question requires you to be selective and concentrate on oxidation and reduction processes.

4 AIR AND ATMOSPHERE

Question	Answer	Mark
1 (a)	Gas X – carbon dioxide; Gas Y – oxygen. Both required.	**1**
(b)	Respiration and combustion of carbon compounds produce carbon dioxide.	**1**
	Photosynthesis removes carbon dioxide and adds oxygen to keep the oxygen-carbon dioxide balance.	**1**
2 (a)	Carbon dioxide	**1**
(b)	Decay of organic waste in landfill sites/marshes/compost heaps/released by termites or cows. (any one)	**1**
(c)	Sulphur dioxide from the factory reacts with water (and oxygen) in the air to make sulphurous and sulphuric acids.	**1**
	Sulphurous acid and sulphuric acid attack the stonework	**1**

Examiner's tip A good answer here could include some equations.

$SO_2(g) + H_2O(l) \rightleftharpoons H_2SO_3(aq)$

$H_2SO_3(aq) + [O] \rightarrow H_2SO_4(aq)$

If the stonework was calcium carbonate

$CaCO_3(s) + H_2SO_4(aq) \rightarrow CaSO_4(s) + H_2O(l) + CO_2(g)$

(d)	Immediately after 1956 levels of sulphur dioxide fell very little.	**1**
	Immediately after 1968 the levels of sulphur dioxide dropped considerably	**1**

Examiner's tip It is easy to drop a mark here. You must make some sort of comparison between what happened after 1956 and after 1968. A one mark answer could be 'the level of sulphur dioxide dropped off after 1968'.

Question	Answer	Mark
3 (a)	Propane	1

Examiner's tip Remember we are dealing with negative numbers.

(b) (i)

$$\overset{\times\times}{\underset{\times\times}{\times}} \text{Cl} \overset{\times}{\underset{}{\times}}$$

$$\overset{\times\times}{\underset{\times\times}{\times}} \text{F} \overset{\circ\times}{\underset{\times\circ}{\times}} \text{C} \overset{\times}{\underset{\times}{\circ}} \text{F} \overset{\times\times}{\underset{\times\times}{\times}}$$

$$\overset{\times}{\underset{\times\times}{\times}} \text{Cl} \overset{\times}{\underset{}{\times}}$$

	Correct arrangement of atoms	1
	Correct arrangement of electrons	1
(ii)	Covalent bonding	1
(iii)	CFCs destroy the ozone layer	3
	CFCs break up to give chlorine atoms	
	Chlorine atoms react and destroy ozone	
	Ozone removes most dangerous UV radiation from Sun	
	Holes in ozone layer over poles	

Examiner's tip Any 3 points are given a mark each. In this kind of question candidates produce a wide range of answers. Any answer that is correct chemistry will receive credit, even if not given on the mark scheme.

(iv)	Propane	1
	It has a boiling point very similar to that of CFC. It is the boiling point which is important in a change from liquid to gas	1

5 QUANTITATIVE CHEMISTRY

Question	Answer	Mark
1 (a) (i)	Number of moles of NaOH $= 0.50 \times 22/1000$	1
	$= 0.011$ moles	1
(ii)	0.011 moles NaOH react with 0.011 moles ethanoic acid	1
	This is dissolved in $10\,cm^3$ of solution	1
	Concentration $= 1000 \times 0.011/10$	1
	$= 1.1\ mol/dm^3$	1
(iii)	Mass of 1 mole of ethanoic acid $= 60\,g$ (*see Unit 6*)	1
	Concentration $= 60 \times 1.1 = 66\,g/dm^3$	1

Question	Answer	Mark

(b)   (i)   24 g of magnesium produces $24\,000\,cm^3$ of hydrogen at r.t.p.   **1**
             0.3 g Mg produces $0.3 \times 24000/24\,cm^3$ hydrogen   **2**
             $= 300\,cm^3$ **1**

   (ii)   From equation, 1 mole of magnesium (24 g)   **1**
             reacts with 2 moles ethanoic acid ($1000\,cm^3$ 2 M acid)   **1**
             0.3 g Mg reacts with $0.3 \times 1000/24\,cm^3$ of acid   **1**
             $= 12.5\,cm^3$ **1**

(c)   (i)   Ethyl ethanoate   **1**

   (ii)   **2**
        (allow 1 mark for slight mistake)

$$H-\underset{\underset{H}{|}}{\overset{\overset{H}{|}}{C}}-C\overset{O}{\underset{O-\underset{\underset{H}{|}}{\overset{\overset{H}{|}}{C}}-\underset{\underset{H}{|}}{\overset{\overset{H}{|}}{C}}-H}{}$$

(d)   (i)   Animal and vegetable fats and oils (not petroleum oils)   **1**

   (ii)   Butter and margarine   **2**
            Flavouring and smells in foods   (Any 2
            Solvents   points)

2   (a)

Question			Answer	Mark
			A labelled circuit with switch, bulb, battery	1
			Anode and cathode correctly labelled	1
			Suitable heated container for calcium bromide	1
(b)	(i)		Quantity of electricity passed = current × time	1
			= 5 × 193 = 965 coulombs	1
	(ii)		Number of Faradays = 965/96500 = 0.01 Faradays	1
	(iii)		2 Faradays of electricity produce 1 mole of calcium atoms	1
			0.01 Faradays produce 0.005 moles of calcium atoms	1
	(iv)		1 Faraday of electricity produces 1 mole of bromine atoms	1
			0.01 Faradays of electricity produce 0.01 moles of bromine atoms	1
(c)			The gap between the electrodes is filled with calcium which conducts electricity	1
(d)			Hydrogen gas	1
			Formed by reaction of calcium with water	1
			$Ca + 2H_2O \rightarrow Ca(OH)_2 + H_2$	1

3	(a)		Pipette (*measuring cylinder not accurate enough*)	1
	(b)		Indicator (methyl orange) changes colour	1
	(c)		$Na_2CO_3(aq) + 2HCl(aq) \rightarrow 2NaCl(aq) + CO_2(g) + H_2O(l)$	1
				1

> **Examiner's tip** Phenolphthalein is another indicator but it changes colour at a higher pH when the following reaction takes place
>
> $$Na_2CO_3(aq) + HCl(aq) \rightarrow NaHCO_3(aq) + NaCl(aq)$$
>
> The volume of acid required for this process is half the volume required when using methyl orange as indicator.

	(d)		$20.0\,cm^3$ of 0.25 M hydrochloric acid	
			Number of moles in $1000\,cm^3$ of 0.25 M acid = 0.25	
			No. of moles in $20\,cm^3$ of 0.25 M acid = 0.25 × 20/1000	1
			= 0.005 moles	1
	(e)		0.005 moles of acid reacts with $25\,cm^3$ of sodium carbonate	
			0.005 × 1000/25 moles of acid react with $1000\,cm^3$ sodium carbonate solution	1
			= 0.2 moles	1
	(f)		From the equation, 2 moles of acid react with 1 mole of sodium carbonate	1
			No. of moles of sodium carbonate = 0.1 moles	1
	(g)		Mass of sodium carbonate = $0.1 \times M_r(Na_2CO_3)$	1
			= 10.6 g	1
	(h)		$10.6\,g\ Na_2CO_3,\ 18\,g\ H_2O$	1
	(i)		180 g	1
	(j)		10	1

Question	Answer	Mark

Examiner's tip This could be a difficult calculation but splitting it into stages helps you to work through it.

4 **(a)** The solutes will dissolve faster in warm water | 1

(b) Sodium hydroxide solution is 80 g/l (or 80 g per dm^3)
1 mole of sodium hydroxide = (23 + 16 + 1) = 40 g | 1
Concentration of sodium hydroxide = 80/40 = 2 mol/1 | 1

(c) For cold brown colour:
10 cm^3 of sodium sulphide solution is added to 40 cm^3 of sodium hydroxide solution to make 50 cm^3 of toner
20 cm^3 of sodium sulphide solution is added to 80 cm^3 of sodium hydroxide solution to make 100 cm^3 of toner | 1
Solution contains $20 \times 100/1000 = 2$ g of sodium sulphide | 1

5 **(a)** **(i)** No calcium carbonate remains in the solution | 1

No bubbles of carbon dioxide are being produced. | 1

Examiner's tip Excess dilute hydrochloric acid tells us that all of the calcium carbonate would be used up when the reaction stops.

(ii) It is possible that some solid remains in the flask. These are impurities which do not react with acid. | 1

(b) $H^+ (aq) + OH^- (aq) \rightarrow H_2O(l)$ | 2

Examiner's tip There are two marks for the correct balanced equation including state symbols. One mark is awarded for a slight mistake. This ionic equation is very important.

(c) **(i)** Mass of hydrochloric acid = 20.00 − 2.48 = 17.52 g | 1

(ii) Mass of 1 mole of $CaCO_3$ = 40 + 12 + (3x16) = 100 g | 1

From the equation

73 g of hydrochloric acid react with 100 g of calcium carbonate | 1

17.52 g of hydrochloric acid reacts with $100 \times \frac{17.52}{73}$ g $CaCO_3$ | 1

$= 24.0$ g | 1

(iii) Percentage purity of calcium carbonate = $100 \times \frac{24.0}{25.0} = 96\%$ | 1

Examiner's tip It is worthwhile looking at your answer and checking it is reasonable.

6 THE PERIODIC TABLE

Question			Answer	Mark

1 (a) (i) **Y**

        (ii) **V**

        (iii) **X**   **3**

  (b)   **V** has the smallest atoms   **1**

          Atomic radius increases down a group   **1**

          Atomic radius decreases across a period from left to right   **1**

> **Examiner's tip** Students can usually appreciate the change down a group as extra shells of electrons are added, e.g. lithium 2,1 and sodium 2,8,1. However, the change across a period is harder to see. Remember as you go across a period the electrons are going in the same shell: lithium 2,1; beryllium 2,2;... fluorine 2,7; neon 2,8. There is no reason for them to be larger. Also every time there is an extra proton in the nucleus, so the force of attraction on the electrons is greater, pulling them closer to the nucleus.

  (c)   (i) **XY**

        (ii) $\mathbf{X_2W}$ **2**

  (d)   (i) *You may want to refer to Unit 5 for this part.*

          0.72 g magnesium combine with 0.28 g Z   **1**

          0.72/24 moles of magnesium combine with 0.28/14 moles Z

          0.03 moles of magnesium combine with 0.02 moles Z   **1**

> **Examiner's tip** It is at this point that many students go wrong and write down a formula Mg_2Z_3. Remember there are three magnesium atoms for every two Z atoms.

          Formula Mg_3Z_2 **1**

      (ii) Period 2; Group V   **2**

          Formula Mg_3Z_2 suggests Z^{3-} ions, so 3 electrons have to be added to get a noble gas electron arrangement   **1**

          $A_r = 14$. Using your Periodic Table you can identify the element as nitrogen and its place in group V   **1**

---

2 (a)   **A**   **1**

  (b)   **E**   **1**

  (c)   **C** and **D**. Both required.   **1**

> **Examiner's tip** E and F are gases. However, F is in Group 0 and elements in Group 0 are composed of single atoms rather than pairs of atoms. If you are confused about groups and periods you could give B and F incorrectly for (c).

---

3 (a)   Barium, strontium, calcium, magnesium   **1**

Question	Answer	Mark

For some syllabuses (AEB and WJEC) you are expected to know some Chemistry of Group II (alkaline earth metals). Other syllabuses do not require you to study this group particularly but you would be expected to answer this question using your knowledge of trends within the Periodic Table. Make sure you put them is order of decreasing reactivity as stated. Many students get the right sequence but put them in order of increasing reactivity. No marks for this!

(b) Reacts very slowly with cold water   1

Examiner's tip You should use the pattern of reactivity in the table to predict this reaction. Any answer which implies less reaction than magnesium would be acceptable -even no reaction.

(c) Under petroleum oil   1

Examiner's tip You should appreciate the reactivity of barium is similar to that of alklai metals. It could perhaps be stored in a similar way.

(d) (i) Barium chloride; $BaCl_2$ 2

   (ii) Ionic bonding   1
         Ba^{2+} and Cl^- 1
         Barium, two e^- in outer energy level are lost to form ion; Cl gains one
         e^- to form Cl^- 1

7 RATES OF REACTION

Question	Answer	Mark

1 (a) **D**   1

Examiner's tip There are different ways of coming up with the correct answer here. One way is to notice that C, D and F take place at 40°C and the others at 20°C. In C and D a powder is used and so reactions will be faster. In D the acid is 4 mol/l rather than 1 mol/l.

(b) **A and E**. Both required.   1

Examiner's tip You should be looking for two reactions where all the conditions are the same except one uses lumps and one uses powder. In some other possible pairs, e.g. B and D or E and F one reaction is at 20° C and the other 40° C.

2 (a) There is no need to collect the gas produced and a flask standing on a top-pan balance is a minimum – worth 1 mark. Usually we put a piece of cotton wool in the flask to prevent the escape of liquid spray, not to prevent the escape of gas   2

(b) (i) Escape of carbon dioxide gas (*see equation*)   1

Question	Answer	Mark

(ii)

Time (min)	Loss of mass (g) large lumps	Loss of mass (g) small lumps
0	0	0
0.5	0.8	2.4
1	1.3	3.3
2	2.2	4.2
3	2.8	4.4
4	3.3	4.4
5	3.7	4.4
6	3.9	4.4

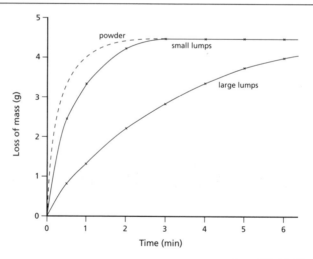

Axes (1) Plotting (2) Curves (2)   **5**

(iii) Shown on graph by dotted line   **2**

(c)   *You may refer to Unit 5 to help you*
From the equation, 1 mole of calcium carbonate (100 g) reacts with
2 moles of hydrochloric acid   **1**
10 g of calcium carbonate react with 0.2 moles HCl   **1**
0.2 moles of HCl is 200 cm^3 (0.2 dm^3) of M acid   **1**

(d) (i) Twice as many H$^+$ ions in solution   **1**
Twice as many collisions between H$^+$ and solid   **1**

Question	Answer	Mark

<table>
<tr><td colspan="2">Examiner's tip The rate of the reaction is determined by the number of collisions between H⁺ ions in the acid and the solid.</td><td></td></tr>
</table>

(ii)	H$^+$ ions possess greater kinetic energy (move faster) and so collide more with solid. More successful collisions.	1

8 INDUSTRIAL PROCESSES

Question	Answer	Mark
1 (a) (i)	Fractional distillation (of air)	1
(ii)	Haber process (or synthesis)	1
(iii)	Neutralization	1
(b)	Fertilizer	1
(c)	Temperature about 450 °C	1
	High pressure (up to 1000 atm)	1
	Catalyst – finely divided iron	1

Examiner's tip It is important that you know the conditions for the Haber process.

(d) (i)	Exothermic reaction	1
(ii)	17 tonnes produces $1 + 14 + (3 \times 16)$ tonnes of nitric acid	1
	= 63 tonnes	1

Examiner's tip Examiners are required to set questions testing social, economic, technological and environmental aspects of Chemistry. Questions on industrial processes provide good opportunities.

2

Examiner's tip This question is about the content of Unit 3. It, however, concentrates on some of the economic and environmental aspects of the process.

(a) (i)	Bauxite has to be purified before electrolysis	2
	Uses a high temperature	(Any 2
	Large quantity of electricity required	points)
(ii)	Scars on the landscape caused by mining of bauxite	3
	Dumped impurities (largely iron oxide) after purification	(Any 3
	Air pollution (caused by fluorides) from aluminium smelter	points)
	More fossil fuels burned	
	More carbon dioxide released	

Question	Answer	Mark
	Factories take up larger land area More claims for hydro-electric power destroy valleys/villages	
(b) (i)	$Al^{3+} + 3e^- \rightarrow Al$	2
(ii)	Combining this equation and the formula for alumina given in the question: $4Al^{3+} + 6O^{2-} \rightarrow 4Al + 3O_2$	1
	(4×27) g of aluminium are produced when (3×32) g of oxygen are produced	1
	So $(4 \times 27)/3$ g of aluminium are produced when 32 g of oxygen are produced	
	$= 36$ g of aluminium	1

Examiner's tip The extraction of aluminium and iron are frequent topics examined at GCSE. Note that the calculation in (b)(ii) relies on getting the correct reacting relationship (or equation) for the decomposition of bauxite.

	Alternatively, you could answer: 1 mole of O_2 produced releases 4 moles of electrons	1
	4 moles of electrons produce 4/3 mole of aluminium	1
	$= 27 \times 4/3 = 36$ g	1

9 WATER

Question	Answer	Mark
1 (a)	Add soap solution	1
	Calcium hydrogencarbonate forms scum, no lather	1
	Distilled water lathers	1
	$Ca^{2+} + 2St^- \rightarrow Ca(St)_2$ St representing anionic part of soap	1
	or	
	Evaporate to dryness	1
	Calcium hydrogencarbonate decomposes to form white residue of calcium carbonate	1
	Distilled water leaves no residue	1
	$Ca(HCO_3)_2(aq) \rightarrow CaCO_3(s) + H_2O(l) + CO_2(g)$	1

Examiner's tip In a question of this type there are always alternative answers which will be given credit.

(b)	Add dilute hydrochloric acid	1
	Sodium carbonate reacts, fizzes, produces carbon dioxide	1
	Sodium hydroxide produces no carbon dioxide	1
	$Na_2CO_3(aq) + 2HCl(aq) \rightarrow 2NaCl(aq) + CO_2(g) + H_2O(l)$	1

Examiner's tip Both have a pH greater than 7 and cannot be distinguished with indicators. Many candidates try to do this. It is not true to say sodium hydroxide does not react. It does react, to produce sodium chloride and water, but there is no gas produced.

Question	Answer	Mark
(c)	Add dilute nitric acid and silver nitrate solution	1
	Hydrochloric acid gives a white precipitate of silver chloride which turns purple in sunlight and dissolves completely in concentrated ammonia solution	1
	Sulphuric acid – no precipitate	1
	$HCl(aq) + AgNO_3(aq) \rightarrow AgCl(s) + HNO_3(aq)$	1

Examiner's tip Both are acids so any general property of an acid (indicators, carbonates, bases, metals) will not be suitable. If you realize one is a chloride and the other a sulphate, you are well on the way. Make sure you suggest acidifying with nitric acid and not hydrochloric acid. If you acidify with hydrochloric acid you are adding chloride ions and will *always* get a positive chloride test!

	or Add dilute hydrochloric acid and barium chloride solution	1
	Hydrochloric acid gives no precipitate	1
	Sulphuric acid gives a white precipitate of barium sulphate	1
	$H_2SO_4(aq) + BaCl_2(aq) \rightarrow BaSO_4(s) + 2HCl(aq)$	1
(d)	*Refer to Unit 8.* Add bromine solution	1
	Hexane, no colour change	1
	Hexene, bromine changes from red to colourless	1
	$C_6H_{12} + Br_2 \rightarrow C_6H_{12}Br_2$ (dibromohexane)	1

Examiner's tip This is an addition reaction to an alkene.

2 (a)	$(NH_4)_3PO_4$	1
(b)	Nitrogen, phosphorus, potassium (all three)	1
(c)	Mass of 1 mole of ammonium nitrate = 80 g	
	Mass of 1 mole of urea = 60 g	Both for **1**
	Percentage of N in ammonium nitrate = $100 \times 28/80 = 35\%$	1
	Percentage of N in urea = $100 \times 28/60 = 46.6\%$	1

Examiner's tip Having calculated the mass of 1 mole of ammonium nitrate and urea by adding relative atomic masses (look at Unit 6 if this causes you problems) you could argue that the percentage of nitrogen in urea will be greater because both contain 28g of N per mole and 1 mole of urea has a smaller mass. This would be worth full marks without doing the tedious calculations.

(d)	Ammonium nitrate being more soluble will be quicker acting	1
(e) (i)	water + urea → ammonia + carbon dioxide	1
(ii)	$H_2O + CO(NH_2)_2 \rightarrow 2NH_3 + CO_2$	3

Examiner's tip One mark for correct formulae on left-hand side and one for correct formulae on right-hand side. One mark for balancing correctly.

Question	Answer	Mark
(f)	*A sample answer worth four marks could be as follows*:	
	Excess fertilizer is washed into rivers and it affects the life in the river in several ways. Bacteria in the water oxidize ammonia to nitrate. In doing this they reduce the dissolved oxygen in the water, which kills fish. Nitrogen also encourages the growth of plants, which block the entry of light into the river so stopping photosynthesis which produces oxygen. Plants decaying also remove oxygen.	4

				Mark
3	(a)		81 g	1
	(b)		33 g	1
	(c)		48 g	1
	(d)		Filter off the potassium dichromate crystals	1
			Wash with a small volume of water and dry	1

> **Examiner's tip** Quantitative interpretation of solubility curves is an important aspect of Higher tier papers.

				Mark
4	(a)	(i)	Calcium hydrogencarbonate	1

> **Examiner's tip** You should know that calcium hydrogencarbonate causes temporary hardness in water. However, the high concntration of calcium and hydrogencarbonate ions in the sample is a good clue.

				Mark
		(ii)	Addition of sodium carbonate crystals	1
			Sodium carbonate precipitates calcium sulphate and removes calcium ions in solution.	1

$$CaSO_4(aq) + Na_2CO_3(aq) \rightarrow CaSO_4(s) + Na_2SO_4(aq)$$

or $\quad Ca^{2+}(aq) + SO_4^{2-}(aq) \rightarrow CaSO_4(s)$ 1

> **Examiner's tip** Note the question is now about permanent hardness. Some candidates will not read this and give a good answer for temporary hardness and receive no marks.

			Mark
(b)		Calcium carbonate	1
(c)		When soap is added to hard water, a precipitate of calcium stearate is formed. This uses up the soap and reduces lather.	

$$2C_{17}H_{35}COO^- Na^+ + Ca^{2+}(aq) \rightarrow (C_{17}H_{35}COO^-)_2Ca^{2+} + 2Na^{2+}$$

Calcium stearate is scum.   3